Any
man
can

Any man can

The Revolutionary New Multiple-Orgasmic Technique For Every Loving Man

Dr William Hartman
and
Marilyn Fithian

ANGUS
& ROBERTSON
PUBLISHERS

ANGUS & ROBERTSON
PUBLISHERS

Unit 4, Eden Park, 31 Waterloo Road,
North Ryde, NSW, Australia 2113
and
16 Golden Square, London
W1R 4BN, United Kingdom

First published in the United States
of America by St Martin's Press in 1984
First published in Australia by
Angus & Robertson Publishers in 1985
First published in the United
Kingdom by Angus & Robertson
(UK) Ltd in 1985

National Library of Australia
Cataloguing-in-publication data.

Hartman, William E., 1919-
    Any man can.

    Bibliography.
    ISBN 0 207 15146 6.
    ISBN 0 207 15073 7 (pbk — not
    available in Australia).

    1. Sex instruction for men. 2. Orgasm.
    I. Fithian, Marilyn A. II. Title.

613.9'6'024041

Printed in Singapore

We are pleased to dedicate this book
to the thirty-three multi-orgasmic men who were willing
to be monitored in our research laboratory.

CONTENTS

ACKNOWLEDGMENTS

The authors gratefully acknowledge the assistance of the following persons in making this book a reality.

Our agent, Sandra Watt, went far beyond the call of duty to acquaint herself with our work and made perceptive suggestions on our written proposal.

Iris Bancroft polished, rewrote, and "popularized" our manuscript and made it acceptable to our publisher.

Ann Miller typed our original version of the manuscript.

Larry M. Davis, M.D., Beverly Deal, R.N., John Hartman, Earle M. Marsh, M.D., Maxie C. Maultsby, Jr., M.D., Jeff Patterson, M.D., Bishara Shahin, Psy., D., J. Jones Stewart, M.D., Barbie Taylor, Ph.D., Delores Wilson, and James L. Young read all or parts of the manuscript with suggestions for improvement or reactions to it. Julius H. Winer, M.D., and Berry Campbell, Ph.D., were consulted for physiological information. Dr. Campbell worked with us in monitoring subjects and interpreting the physiological data.

Nick Konnoff utilized special skills in analyzing some of the data on a computer. References to his unpublished papers are made in the Bibliography.

The manuscript was improved substantially by the editorial suggestions of Tom Dunne and Lisa Wager.

This book would not have been possible without the information received from clients and research subjects at the Center for Marital and Sexual Studies. We respect their privacy and accordingly have changed names and other clearly identifiable personal or social characteristics and composites were made.

INTRODUCTION

Most men today are well aware of the deluge of literature dealing with female sexuality that has appeared in the last ten years. There has been enough, in fact, to make many normal men give up in despair. How much motivation can there be for a man to enter into sexual encounters that demand hours of work on his part—with only a few moments of pleasure as his reward?

Very little.

Yet, till now it has appeared—at least from the literature available—that this was the best a man could hope for. Books and sex clinics challenged him to learn the meaning of being a "gentle man," and informed him that he would get his pleasure in proportion to the pleasure he gave his partner. The emphasis was on the frustration of women mated to men who ejaculated "too soon" after vaginal penetration. Male readers were reminded of their responsibility to give their female partners optimum satisfaction, whatever the cost to them in time and effort.

A dismally unequal situation, certainly.

Yet, it isn't surprising that for the last decade or two much emphasis has been directed exclusively toward women's satisfaction. Most unbalanced situations swing like pendulums for a time before true equilibrium is reached:

for too many years prior to the 1960s many women had been excluded from sexual pleasure entirely.

The result, however, was the creation of sexual "princesses," who often intimidated their male partners with their expectations for sexual "service." As the inequity increased, the time came closer when, of necessity, consideration had to be given to the male's pleasure. It was no more right that he should be a "sex servant" to a woman than that she should be his erotic pawn.

Early in their research, begun in the late sixties, William Hartman and Marilyn Fithian, co-directors of The Center for Marital and Sexual Studies, realized that some of their male subjects received as much sexual pleasure from lengthy periods of lovemaking as did their partners. These men were not simply doers, stimulating wildly orgasmic princesses. They were experiencing as many orgasmic peaks as they provided their partners. And because their pleasure and that of their partners was mutual, they seemed more able to feel true intimacy. It was these men who inspired the research that led to this book on multi-orgasms for men.

When the Center for Marital and Sexual Studies in Long Beach, California, was first established, the advisory board agreed that Hartman and Fithian should "research human sexual behavior in the laboratory and treat sexual dysfunction." Both they and the board assumed that most of their efforts would be directed toward the treatment of sexual dysfunction—and so they were.

However, they soon realized that many of the men and women who came to them for help were totally unable to communicate with others in any nonverbal manner, let alone sexually. They wanted to touch and show affection, but they didn't know how. Often they didn't even dare to try for fear of being rebuffed, or because they assumed that any physical contact would inevitably lead to intercourse. Some had a deep inner conditioning against entering into any form of physical closeness. To help these clients, Hartman and Fithian developed a treatment process that involved a gradual introduction to touching and caressing without any demand that such contact lead to actual intercourse until both partners had grown accustomed to close nonsexual physical contact. A report on that technique was published in *Treatment of Sexual Dysfunction.*

Why approach sexual problems by such a path? Because Hartman and Fithian learned very quickly that most of their clients had a desire to express affection, but felt inept at doing so. They wanted more than just to improve their sexual performance. They wanted to learn how to share their feelings. They wanted to be freed of inhibiting conditioning so their sexual encounters would become expressions of the deep love they felt for each other. And they wanted these expressions of affection to be released from the anxiety that demands for certain levels of performance put upon them. The nondemand caressing approach to sexual difficulties advocated by Hartman and Fithian usually solved the problems.

With such a beginning, it is logical that the primary goal of the Center should remain that of helping clients to achieve a warm intimacy that will give sparkle and joy to their lives. Since mutual sexual pleasure is a desired aspect of that intimacy, it is also logical that Hartman and Fithian should turn to the problem presented by the great disparity between male and female sexual behavior.

A feeling of warmth and intimacy grows when a couple is not rushed—and when both partners have a true desire to extend the time they spend in lovemaking. If a man sees sex as a five-minute dash to ejaculation and the woman is hoping for hours of pleasure, they certainly cannot reach any mutually satisfactory form of sexual communication.

So this book is only incidentally a "how-to" book. Far more important to the happiness of the couples who will read it is what is said about intimacy and its relationship to mutuality. No union can work if one partner is forever giving and the other receiving. There must be a balance. When a man can share in the soaring experience of multiple orgasms, he will have less reason to resent the demands that satisfying his partner put upon him. Working together in this way, a man and woman will mutually reach the ecstasy of true fulfillment.

There are definite steps a man needs to take to master this technique. It begins, obviously, with personal effort and a strong desire for improvement. As a man develops the ability to enjoy extended sexual contact, he also becomes more open to experience the thrill of sharing true warmth, closeness, and emotional intimacy. With such rewards ahead, the effort involved seems small, indeed.

1

What Are We Talking About?

We're talking about men sharing in the delight of having one orgasm after another. We're talking about an end to the painful tension that exists when a man, knowing that his partner has had sex with other men, finds himself in desperate competition with these unknown lovers. We're suggesting that a man who himself wants to extend sex play because it gives him pleasure will please a woman far more than even the most talented lover who performs out of duty or from a sense of competition. To help our readers reach this goal, we must first clear up a few misconceptions about male sexuality.

The strongest impediment most men must overcome when they think of multi-orgasms for themselves is the belief that orgasm and ejaculation are inextricably bound together. This belief seems to have originated in Western culture at about the same time as the concept of female indifference to sex. We have disproved the latter, as the many books on the subject attest. It is time now to tackle the first—and possibly the most insidious—idea, and lay it forever to rest.

Ejaculation and male orgasm are *not* synonymous. We learned this in our laboratory, when thirty-three different men claimed that they were multi-orgasmic—and proved their contention. Recordings confirmed that during one session these men could reach recognizable orgasm again and again—just as some women could. In fact, unless we looked at the name of the subject, we could not tell whether a chart we studied was that of a female or male multi-orgasmic response.

Our curiosity stirred, we studied the charts of other male subjects who had not claimed the ability to have multi-orgasms but who had very successful sex relationships. A number of those showed similar peaks, leading us to conclude that they probably also had multiple orgasms, of which they were not aware because they believed orgasm and ejaculation were synonymous and they did not ejaculate at every peak. This indicated to us that male multiple orgasms were more common than we first believed them to be.

Our next breakthrough came over a period of years. We often lecture in the United States and abroad, and whenever we discussed the idea of male multiple orgasms, we encountered a great deal of interest. Always, one or two men would come up to us after our lecture and inform us that they, too, were multi-orgasmic. Interestingly, the greatest response came from groups of men who were involved in hypnosis, especially if they were skilled in self-hypnosis. This isn't surprising. One must know how to relax before one can master multi-orgasmic response, just as one must relax to go into a state of self-hypnosis.

Can Every Man Do It?

Soon after completing our study of the initial thirty-three men, we realized that they had all learned to have multiple orgasms, either by accident or deliberately. This was not entirely unexpected. Most sexual functions appear to be learned. Even people who receive no organized instruction (and that includes many of us, even today) learn through reading, through "discussions" with peers, and through jokes and films. Obviously, the better the instruction, the more skilled the student becomes. So the second concept that is important for a man who wishes to learn to be multi-orgasmic is this: Others have learned to be multi-orgasmic —you can, too.

The third bit of misinformation that must be corrected before we can continue is very deep-seated. From the time we are infants we are taught that men and women—boys and girls—are very different. On "face value" that statement seems irrefutable. However, a quick review of the genital development of a fetus will show just how wrong that belief is.

At conception, the fetus has no sex. It is simply a living organism with undeveloped organs. At five weeks this changes. What appears where the genitals will eventually grow is a series of folds in the outer skin and primitive inner organs that most resemble those of the female. In fact, were one to try to determine sex of the fetus at five weeks one would have to assume it was female.

During the sixth and seventh weeks, the female fetus shows a refinement in the clitoris and the folds of skin that will become the labia minor and labia major. In the male fetus, the "clitoral stem" begins to grow, forming a tiny penis, and the folds of skin that make up the labia in the female close up to form a sac. If you're a male, look at your scrotum and penis. You will see a fine line, called a raphe, which is the seam line created at that time in the development of the male fetus. On maturity, the testicles move down into the sac created by this "seaming" of the raphe.

Meanwhile, inside the body of the female fetus the fallopian tubes and the ovaries are developing. Those same tubes and sacs, in the male fetus, change into the testicles and the tubing that will carry sperm from its place of origin to the penis. So tiny are these developments that it is not possible to tell with certainty the sex of an unborn child until it is at least eleven weeks old. So the third idea we must learn is this: Men and women—boys and girls—are more alike than they are different.

There are some other things we ought to consider. For one thing, it is easy to see that since many more—and much greater—changes take place in a male fetus than in a female, there are more opportunities for problems to develop. Some men have one testicle that never descends into the scrotum when they mature. Some men have the urethral opening on the underside of the penis head (called hypospadias) or on the top side (called epispadias), rather than at the very end. However, these small imperfections do not generally interfere with normal living, nor are they uncommon. In our work, we have encountered a dozen or so men who have some such minor imperfection in penile structure. None of them have found it to be a handicap. It is, in fact, usually not even noticeable unless one is carefully examining the penis.

It's important to recognize that men with such a condition can still use the squeeze technique we describe later. However, instead of placing their fingers as we illustrate, they should place them under the urethral opening, toward the base of the penis.

What Do We Mean by Orgasm?

We define orgasm as a peak in emotional and physical responses, accompanied by pelvic contractions, experienced during sexual stimulation. We do not expect male orgasm to be accompanied always by ejaculation. This is a legitimate definition, used by other researchers. To determine just when orgasm takes place, we check our subjects' responses with the use of a Beckman R411 dynograph.

We use heart-rate peak as the clearest method of identifying orgasm. Usually the heart rate at rest will be about 70 beats per minute. It will speed up to about 120 beats during orgasm, and return to 70 beats when orgasm is over. A typical chart of a female during orgasm resembles a bell-shaped curve, with the actual duration of orgasm usually being from about six to thirty seconds. The longest orgasm observed lasted one minute.

Some women have several such peaks, interspersed with "valleys." We call such repeating of orgasms multiple orgasms, discrete (see page 160). That is, they start at "rest," or baseline, reach a peak, and return to baseline before another peak occurs.

Another group of women have an entirely different pattern of multiple orgasms. Their heart rates do not drop to baseline between peaks, but stay high. This is called multi-orgasms, continuous. Yet the peaks are easily identified both by us and by the subjects (see page 161). Another pattern we find is one where the woman has a number of discrete orgasms and then a multi-orgasm with little drop in heartbeat between peaks.

Probably because of the emphasis placed on female response during the years of our research, we have far more samples from female subjects than from males. However, even with our smaller male samplings we can detect certain definite similarities between male and female responses. Though individual reactions indicate a "fingerprinting" effect of sexual response for any one individual, there are still certain overall patterns that can easily be identified. It has become clear to us that the similarities between male and female sexual responses are far greater than most people expect them to be.

Sex is a physical activity, and each individual behaves differently—with different response times and varying periods needed before orgasm occurs. Some of our female subjects had their first orgasms after only three minutes of self-stimulation. Others needed almost an hour. The aver-

5

age period was about twenty minutes. But for all the women tested, the actual time span for any given orgasm was quite short—not more than one minute in duration.

Anyone who has read about male orgasms knows that this is the average duration of male orgasm as well—another indication of the similarity between male and female sexual behavior that has been ignored in most reports—until now.

Why Shouldn't Men Be Multi-Orgasmic?

Throughout our research, one thing has become clear. There are many differences existing in female sexual responses, yet it appears that most women either are, or can be, multi-orgasmic. As we considered the identical origins of the sex organs in the male and female fetus, we began seriously to question the conclusion, so generally accepted by both the scientific and lay communities, that men could only have one orgasm in any one sexual encounter while women naturally could have many. Our findings that the scientific "picture" of a male orgasm bore a strong resemblance to that of a female served to further reinforce our theory that men could—if they learned how—have as many orgasms as women do during one sexual experience. Subsequent research, over a period of ten years, has shown this to be true.

So, once more, we returned to the analysis of the recorded responses of the multi-orgasmic men who first came to our notice. We compared their scientific "pictures" with those of multi-orgasmic women, and found the same patterns existed. Some men had more than one orgasm without ever experiencing a marked drop in heartbeat. Others had a number of orgasms in sequence, each separated from the next by the typical drop to "base" heartbeat. Others had a combination of both responses.

These similarities served to remove any doubts we might have had regarding the issue. We are convinced that the only obstacles to a man's experiencing multiple orgasms of one kind or another are his conditioning and his acceptance of the idea that for a man orgasm and ejaculation always come together.

Further inquiry convinced us that even in the area of ejaculation, there is no one "normal" pattern among our multi-orgasmic subjects. Some seem to expel at least a small amount of ejaculate each time they reach a peak. Others only ejaculate when they have their "final" orgasm for the session. In some cases the man experiences what is called a "retrograde ejaculation." When this occurs, the ejaculate does not move out through the penis, but instead is forced back into the bladder, where it remains until the man urinates.

Generally speaking, however, we determined that most multi-orgasmic men do not have what might be termed a "full ejaculation" until they have experienced a number of sexual peaks. So the first goal of a man who wishes to become multi-orgasmic must be to learn to prevent full ejaculation until he is ready to end his sexual encounter.

There's All Kinds

A recent article in a popular magazine notes that one reason why men do not have multiple orgasms is that, when they do, the last orgasm is not as good as the first. That may be true when a full ejaculation occurs with the first orgasm. However, that type of multiple orgasm does not seem to occur very often in laboratory situations.

Many young men know that if they ejaculate early in a sexual encounter they can continue to remain erect if they just keep up the stimulation. We have seen this response in one of our subjects, who ejaculated with each orgasm, continued stimulation until he had another orgasm (also with ejaculation), and who did not lose his erection until he was ready to stop. He had a very short recovery period, for as he lay resting after his first orgasm, as soon as his heartbeat had returned to normal he announced he could "go again." We reset the recorder, and he continued on, having four more orgasms before he was through. This man, in his sexual behavior, closely resembled some of our female subjects.

Anyone wishing to verify these findings can consult the Appendix, where reproductions of the charts of these subjects are printed. They show conclusively the similarity between male and female responses both in individual-orgasmic and in multiple-orgasmic experiences.

Certain other similarities between male and female sexual responses began to show up in our dynograph recordings. For most multi-orgasmic men, the later orgasms were the stronger. This kind of response exactly parallels the experience we have had with females. When they are asked to rate their individual "peaks" in a multi-orgasmic experience, they rate the later orgasms as the more intense.

One interesting point. The men who gave us their subjective analysis of a series of orgasms did not seem to consider the amount of ejaculate expelled each time as very important. In some men the actual amount of ejaculate at each peak was about the same, but nevertheless the later orgasms were considered by them to be the more intense. In others, where ejaculation varied with each orgasm, there seemed to be no correlation between subjective value placed on the orgasm and the amount of ejaculate.

This leads to another important point: Quantity of ejaculate does not determine the quality of the orgasm.

One other point to consider. The multi-orgasmic men we have studied have chosen to develop that capability. They can function equally well with single orgasms. However, they experience multiple orgasms during masturbation as well as when having sex. If the only reason for a man learning to have multiple orgasms is so he can please his partner more, there would be no reason for him to seek multiple orgasms when he was alone. Obviously, a man receives a bonus of pleasure in masturbation when he learns to extend his orgasmic responses.

Another interesting fact is that many of the men who have proven to be multi-orgasmic assume that all men have similar reactions, and so say nothing about their capacity until we remark on it. Rarely do we find that multi-orgasmic men have inflated egos because of that capacity. It is not, in other words, a "macho" response. It is learned as a way of increasing personal pleasure—and of sharing pleasure with another.

Getting Down to Basics

Don't assume that because others have multiple orgasms they can be achieved without effort. Do you desire to learn this skill? Are you motivated to achieve your goal? Do you have the time to develop this skill? If you answer yes to these three questions, we offer here a process that is effective. All you need add beyond those three ingredients is the willingness to think while you are reading and learning, so that you can be aware of your special needs and adapt the process we describe to fit them.

Success in sex is ultimately determined by intimacy—not by the number of orgasms each partner experiences. It also depends on the participants having fun. If, as you move along, you find the fun you have with sex increasing, then you know you are on the right track.

Sex should always be pleasurable. It should bring two people closer together in shared enjoyment. That's why male multi-orgasm is important. A woman and a man moving from one orgasm to another together will feel a closeness never shared in a less ideal situation. And that, certainly, is the ultimate in erotic delight.

2

So Who Cares, Anyway?

To paraphrase Gertrude Stein, "Orgasm is an orgasm is an orgasm." Many people feel that's true. Yet our research has convinced us that orgasms differ in intensity as well as in the satisfaction they give. A woman mated to a man who has no control over when he reaches orgasm often has this complaint, which we hear from many of our female clients: "He just wants his own pleasure. He uses me. He gets it up, puts it in, ejaculates—and it's all over. Where are all the good feelings I'm supposed to have?"

No wonder many women reject sex. No wonder the pat joke "Not tonight, Harry, I have a headache" strikes such a responsive cord in so many hearts.

Yet, is it fair to demand that a man go against what he believes is his nature? Isn't it asking a lot of a busy man, tired from a day's work, that he spend hours "giving" sexual pleasure to his wife through foreplay, when he receives little benefit from what he is doing? It would appear that both the man and the woman in such a situation have a solid basis for a knock-down, drag-out argument.

But argument is not what two people in love want. They want to increase their mutual pleasure, not defend its nonexistence.

One husband we treated described his feelings as he

built up to orgasm. "It's hard for me to take pleasure myself," he explained. "I feel almost guilty about it. I was raised where it was considered sinful." He admitted that he believed the adage "It is more blessed to give than to receive," but that sometimes he had to take his own pleasure despite his recognition that such an act was selfish.

Sex in the Modern Marriage

"If we can't work out our sexual problems, we're going to get a divorce." June, one of our clients, sat stiffly beside her husband. She was very close to tears. "We've been married a year, now, and neither one of us is satisfied sexually. We just don't know what's the matter. We love each other, and we have so much in common. We go to the same church, we both want two children, we come from the same social set. Generally, we want the same things out of life. But sex is important to us both—too important to ignore."

Their sex relationship was marred by the same inequities that affect many unions. Jim felt guilty when he sought satisfaction for himself before June was satisfied, yet he could not continue intercourse long enough to please his wife. Before she married Jim, June had dreamed of nights of ecstasy. Like many women in our society, she had read a number of books dealing with female multi-orgasm, and her expectations were high.

They always indulged in foreplay, hoping it would help June have at least one sexual climax. This often included oral contact and caressing. But Jim could continue such sex play for only a limited time before he felt a need to drive toward his own orgasm.

June and Jim are typical of many of our clients. They know enough to recognize that a problem exists. They might even realize that if they don't solve the problem in their present marriage, it will haunt them in any future relationship they may establish. But they have been unable to find guidance among their peers or their elders, either because they hesitate to ask, or because they can find no one who understands their dilemma.

We found June and Jim to be ideal subjects. With a sound relationship in all areas other than sexual, they were willing to work together to improve their sex lives. They had the motivation, the desire, and the time.

As Jim learned how to have more than one orgasm during one sexual encounter, he was able to satisfy June without feeling "put upon," as he often had when he performed cunnilingus (oral stimulation) for a long period of time.

The breakthrough came when Jim realized that when he used the technique for developing his own multi-orgasmic potential, he did not have to consider his orgasm as putting an end to their shared sexual pleasure. Instead, with June, he built on his first orgasm, bringing them both to new "highs" that gave them more mutual enjoyment.

This couple came to the Center hoping to balance their sexual pleasure, so they could hold on to a marriage that in other ways was happy. What they learned was a new route to greater intimacy, a pathway that enhanced every aspect of their lives.

One Man Alone

Another type of person who makes an ideal "student" of multi-orgasms is the single man. He wants each sexual encounter he has to give both himself and his partner optimum pleasure. Even though he isn't involved in any specific relationship that he wants to preserve, he, too, has the motivation, the desire, and the time to explore his own capabilities for multi-orgasm.

Many single men who have come to us for help acknowledge that they hope to marry sometime in the future. They are looking for skills that will put their sexual relationship on a sound basis at the very beginning, and are convinced that only if they prove to be superior lovers will they get the woman they want.

Follow-up of our single clients has uncovered an interesting fact. Often, after going through our sex therapy program, a man will seem to be more relaxed about sex in general. It is possible that he feels so much more secure in his sexual ability that he no longer has the need to prove himself with every woman he dates. He seems to have less fear, apprehension, and anxiety regarding sex than he had before. When he does again begin a sexual relationship with a woman, that relationship usually results in marriage.

Sex as Recreation—the New Way

Any man or woman who recognizes that sex has recreational value, besides its traditional function of procreation, should be able to accept the importance of balancing all shared sexual pleasure. We live in a world that is developing severe problems caused by overpopulation. It is patently ridiculous to suggest that the ideal cure for this is a cessation of all sex except when children are wanted. The obvious answer is for society to accept recreational sex as valuable, and to encourage individuals to learn all they can to make any sex they have as mutually pleasurable as possible.

For some people, sex has been—and will remain—a way to release tension. And this, too, is a valid use of the activity. But when the element of fun is added, as it is in recreational sex, pleasure is increased while the "tension release" value of the mating is in no way diminished. Under such circumstances, the complaint that sex is exploitive loses its validity.

And when, in the sharing of sexual fun, both partners are capable of enjoying many orgasms, all elements of exploitation disappear.

Most people acknowledge that there are many reasons for enjoying sex. We have mentioned a few—procreation, release of tension, the expressing of affection—but there are many others that rise from the intimate relationships of men and women. Whatever the motivation that brings a male and female together, except possibly the desire for children, the sex they share can be improved when the man matches his partner in his ability to have repeated orgasms. So there are, certainly, quite a few reasons why a man would seek to become multi-orgasmic.

For us, however, only two reasons stand out as critical. First, there is the natural wish any individual has to increase his ability to have pleasure. Second, there is the role multiple orgasms play in developing intimacy. As we have said earlier, the more time spent in close contact, the greater the chance for intimacy.

Intimacy and closeness are, to be sure, far more than sexual technique. But, as is so often the case, the mastery of technique opens the door to greater unity between partners, which, until they both learned to experience the same kind of orgasmic response, was denied to them.

So the answer to the question in the title of this chapter is clear. Men certainly have reason to be interested in learning to have multiple orgasms. Such knowledge will make sex more fun for them, and turn one-sided foreplay into far more pleasurable extended intercourse.

Women have an equally selfish reason for wanting their partners to be multi-orgasmic. One woman remarked that she felt guilty when she asked her man to "give" her more than one orgasm, since he, himself, could have only one. She heard him say he enjoyed performing cunnilingus, but she could never quite believe him. When he learned to have multiple orgasms, her feelings of guilt faded, for she could see that he got as much enjoyment as she did from the long periods they spent sharing sex.

And therein lies the basis of this entire book. As sex counselors and therapists, we want to help men and women develop intimacy in their relationships. We feel that with this pleasurable extension of the time spent in sexual union, a couple can solidify their union. They can explore the fun of togetherness—the richness of total intimacy. And in such a relationship, they can both grow.

3

How Some Men Have Learned It

Sam was a bright ten-year-old exploring his own body when he first learned the pleasure of orgasm. Of course, he didn't ejaculate. He was too young for that. But over and over again he reached a peak of enjoyment such as he had never felt in any other form of play. And it was so easy! All he had to do was continue stimulating his penis after the first intense reaction, and another followed soon after.

When he was eleven and a half he had his first orgasmic ejaculation. It, like the peaks of sexual excitement he had reached before, was very exciting. But it changed things as well. Somehow, he had difficulty going on to the second or third "peak" as he had done before. He continued stimulation, as he had in the past, and did, at last, reach an orgasm. But it was not as satisfying as the second one had been in the past.

From then on, when he masturbated, he deliberately tried to avoid ejaculation the first time. It was not an easy task, but he persisted until, to his intense pleasure, he discovered that he could once more experience the high peaks to which he had become accustomed.

Sam has been multi-orgasmic for twenty years. To him,

it is natural. He was surprised, when he heard us speak, that other men did not share his talent. He can have a single orgasm, if he chooses, when he hasn't enough time to enjoy more. He finds this ability useful for those times when he and his partner have to leave for work or an appointment but wish to share sex before they separate for the day.

To emphasize the contrast between Sam and the conventional picture of a multi-orgasmic male, Sam at first had difficulty relaxing and enjoying himself fully with a partner because he was so aware of her desires and his wish to satisfy her. When he became more at ease during intercourse, he resumed his ability to be multi-orgasmic.

Is Sam unique? He does not appear to be. He is a normal male whose talent for multiple orgasms has been developed almost accidentally. He does, however, have a well-developed pubococcygeous muscle (which we'll shorten right now to "PC" muscle), the muscle that, in both male and female, runs between the pubic bone in front and the coccyx (tail bone) in the back. In the male, this muscle is called the *voluntary urinary sphincter muscle*. However, we will continue to call it the PC muscle, for simplicity's sake.

Sam has always played games with this muscle. As a boy, he used to lie in bed, raising and lowering his penis by tightening and relaxing that muscle. He didn't know its name (and probably wouldn't have been able to pronounce it if he had), but he used it often, enjoying the effects he achieved. He would hang a towel on his penis in the shower room before and after gym, much to the amusement of his friends, and he would make the towel move by tensing his PC muscle.

Our research has shown that a strong PC muscle is necessary if a man is to learn to control his ejaculations. So, unwittingly, Sam did the very thing to keep his multi-orgasmic talent strong. What is important to you, as a reader, is this: Muscles grow strong with exercise. If you want to enjoy multi-orgasms, start right now—while you're reading. Just tighten and relax that muscle between your legs. And then keep on reading.

Ted learned to become multi-orgasmic much later in life. He is an M.D., well acquainted with the physical structure of the body and its functions. When he was thirty, having sex with his wife, he noticed what he felt to be an orgasm without any ejaculation or subsequent loss of erection.

An accident? Maybe he had misinterpreted what he experienced? He wasn't sure.

The next time he was with his wife, he paid more attention to his reactions, deliberately trying to duplicate that "freak" orgasmic sensation that he had felt before. It came while he was thrusting, as he tightened his PC muscle. Yes, the old PC again!

At first he could not be certain he would have what he described as a "dry orgasm." Sometimes it happened, sometimes it didn't. But as he persisted, his skill increased. Now, he and his wife continue lovemaking for an hour or more at a time, a practice common among newlyweds. He believes that his multi-orgasmic ability is responsible for keeping his sex life at a peak usually lost after the first year or so of marriage. We agree.

Sometimes It Comes as a Bonus

Dick became multi-orgasmic as a result of sex therapy. In the session in which we discuss the "nondemand pleasuring" technique, where two people who have been having trouble relating sexually are assigned the task of giving each other physical pleasure with only one taboo—their caressing must not lead to intercourse—Dick seemed reluctant to agree to the assignment. When we added one more aspect to the week's practice—that they use the "squeeze" technique so as to stop Dick from having an orgasm during this pleasuring—he could no longer contain himself.

He informed us that no black man would ever allow his wife to have that much control over him. We hadn't heard this before, but we were not willing to abandon the assignment because of a personal bias. So we suggested that he could apply the pressure himself. We provided him with the directions, and advised him that he could work at contracting his PC muscle as he came close to orgasm, but that since his muscle was not strong, it might take him months to accomplish the control that could be given were he to permit his wife to apply the pressure for him.

What we didn't anticipate was his persistence and his good physical condition. He returned a week later to inform us that he was multi-orgasmic. With justifiable pride he told us that he was "into running," and that he covered from fifteen to twenty miles a day. He hadn't bothered to tell us this before.

He went on to explain that when he first tried to tighten his PC muscle, just before what is termed "ejaculatory inevitability," he discovered to his dismay that he simply hurried his orgasm along. He was annoyed—and embarrassed. But he was not the kind of man to quit after a first failure. He continued to work at it until he mastered the technique.

When he volunteered to be monitored in the laboratory, we accepted. He was right. He had, in one week, become multi-orgasmic. He gave us permission to film him so we could study his technique, and we found that he could control ejaculation either by using the squeeze method or by tightening his PC muscle.

Once, during the filming, he lost his erection without any indication of ejaculating. To discover what had happened, we took a sample of his urine and found that he had had a "retrograde ejaculation," where the ejaculate goes into the bladder instead of being expelled. On a previous occasion, another male who had had a similar experience had provided us with a urine specimen that showed the same results. We speculate that in some cases where there has been no apparent ejaculation and yet the penis loses its rigidity, this same retrograde ejaculation occurs.

If you're interested in more information on this subject, look at the section dealing with retrograde ejaculation in the Appendix. What's important to know is that there is no apparent harm to the body when a retrograde ejaculation takes place. All that happens is that if the ejaculation is complete the penis becomes flaccid, as it usually does after any "normal" ejaculation.

Two things to remember: When you begin to practice the exercises in Chapter Eight, you, too, might at some time have a retrograde ejaculation. Don't let it upset you. Just remember that this isn't your goal. You want to be able to stop ejaculation at will—not just to redirect it.

Another man who developed his multi-orgasmic ability during sex therapy was Tony, a fifty-three-year-old client who had decided that, since he suddenly found himself single again, he wanted to become a super lover so he would have no trouble satisfying the women he dated. He was, to say the least, well motivated.

During the second week, he worked with a surrogate (see page 166), who expected to assist him in mastering what we had taught during the first five sessions. Most clients need help in conquering inhibitions that block sexual relaxation. But not Tony. He had listened when we said that most men probably could be multi-orgasmic if they took the time to learn the skill, and, with his usual enthusiasm and drive, he decided to try for the top.

Like all our clients, he had been put on a regimen of exercises to strengthen the PC and the pelvic muscles. When he began work with his surrogate, he simply decided to "go for" multiple orgasms—and succeeded. Even his surrogate, who had worked with other clients, was surprised at the extra pleasure she received because of his newfound ability.

"I love it," she told us enthusiastically. "I've always had trouble with partners who didn't last long enough for me to have an orgasm. But with Tony I come and come. I have three or four orgasms—and so does he. I've never had this experience before." If a client in therapy can become that capable of satisfying an experienced woman, think how happy you can make your wife.

Even an Impotent Man Can Do It

When we met Tim and his wife, they were on vacation from a distant town. They had come to our clinic to be observed, since they had heard of our need for copulatory data on successful marriages, and felt theirs was close to ideal. Tim was seventy—and completely impotent.

What surprised us was how little his disability affected him or his wife. They shared a rich sex life, and informed us that they both were multi-orgasmic. At our suggestion, they consented to stay near the Center and return the next day for more extensive study. Tim explained that all this was quite exciting for two "old retired people."

The next day they consented to serve as research subjects during lovemaking. Our machines served to confirm their assertions. They were both multi-orgasmic, just as they claimed to be. But what was most interesting to us was their explanation of when all this had started—and the manner in which they reached satisfaction.

Tim had developed diabetes when he was young, and even when they were first married he was totally impotent. He did not, however, allow his disability to destroy him. Instead, he was determined to enjoy and give enjoyment during sex, even if he had to confine himself to oral and manual stimulation. His wife agreed.

"He was uneasy about getting married at all, but I insisted," she said. "After all, I knew I could enjoy all kinds of sex, and I was sure that we could manage to have something special even if he never had an erection. And you can see that we do."

Tim's wife was so at ease during those first crucial nights that Tim soon relaxed. As his enjoyment of oral and manual sex increased, he began to have multi-orgasms. It was that simple. "It's foolish for people to think a man has to have an erection for a couple to have good sex," Tim's wife assured us. "We feel our sex life is great. We get together two or three times a week—and it's always as good as this."

For Tim the crucial ingredient was relaxation. What is also clear is this: A man does not even need to have an erection to experience multi-orgasms.

Can a Handicapped Man Do It?

When Tom came to us with his female partner, we were impressed by the extent of his disability. He had been born with a progressive birth defect. In high school, he had experienced increased difficulty climbing stairs. By the time he came to see us, he was twenty-two, a student at a local university, and totally confined to a wheelchair. He was easily fatigued, had trouble breathing, often had pneumonia, and had a tracheotomy in his throat, to which his respirator (which he usually used only at night) could be attached. He had a full-time live-in aid who cared for most of his physical needs.

Tom heard us give a lecture at his college, during which we spoke of the techniques that should be practiced by a man who wishes to become multi-orgasmic. He began to experiment, practicing the pelvic exercises until he felt certain that he had achieved his goal. He came to us for testing, hoping that our graphs would confirm what he felt sure had happened to him.

He and his partner came in, let us "wire" them to our machines, and proceeded to make love. As he had predicted, they both had multiple orgasms. Yet he had to use his oxygen tank to keep from tiring.

To show us the difference in his success rate when he breathed on his own, he allowed us to detach the tank. Again, his prediction was confirmed. Without the oxygen, he tired too easily, and as a result ejaculated quickly.

His girlfriend was very happy with his newfound skill. "It's great," she insisted. "I could never have an orgasm before. But he goes longer now, and I have time to build to a climax without worrying about him. I sure am glad he went to that lecture."

An Active Partner Helps

One of our subjects, Sandy, was fifty-four when he came to us, sent by a mutual friend who knew we were interested in examining men who were multi-orgasmic. He submitted to our tests and proved to be capable of more than one orgasm at a time.

Sandy had not been alone when he first discovered his multi-orgasmic capabilities. "It was my partner who showed me that I could do it," he explained. "She wouldn't stop making love to me, even after I had an orgasm. And one day it just happened."

Like the others, he showed the typical pattern of multi-orgasmic males, and his responses were documented by us.

We were not surprised to find other men who had had experiences like Sandy's. One, a fifty-eight-year-old man whom we will call Max, became multi-orgasmic when he began to share sex with a woman who refused to stop thrusting when he had an orgasm. Since she preferred the "female-superior" position, she was in control, even when he considered himself finished.

This woman discovered that if she tightened her PC muscle after Max ejaculated, she could keep him erect for from fifteen to twenty minutes longer. The first time this happened, Max was uneasy, but he soon learned to relax and let her "do her thing."

What she did was exactly what we teach in our Center. Immediately after Max's orgasm, she squeezed with her PC muscle, holding still for about twenty seconds. This extended period of inactivity reduced the extreme sensitivity of Max's penis enough so she could move without hurting him.

Then she would begin to move slowly, gradually speeding up until she and Max both reached another peak. Often, they would have their orgasms together, and though they didn't particularly work for this, they claimed it was common. What we noted was that he had more than one orgasm —as did she—during the session they had in our observation room.

One other note: Max's orgasmic responses were always very intense. His body spasmed during orgasm, lifting his head five to six inches off the pillow, and his anus contracted strongly. These observable physical evidences of the success of his partner's procedure were in addition to the records made on our charts.

Do Drugs Help—or Hinder?

Illegal drugs cannot be used in the laboratory. Nevertheless, some of our subjects report that they have smoked marijuana (pot) before coming to the office for testing. Therefore, some of our records do show the effect of drugs on sexual performance. Also, some drugs were in the past legal, and during that time were available for our testing.

One of our subjects, Jay, confessed to us after almost a year as a research subject that when he was at home with a partner he used butyl nitrite to bring him up to a "high" where multiple orgasm could occur.

Why did he wait for a full year before telling us about his "secret" technique? To begin with, he had never considered that his repeated sexual "highs" were true orgasms. Second, he was reluctant to speak of his use of butyl nitrite until he was certain that we would not put him down, not only because of his use of the drug, but because of the circumstances in which he resorted to it.

Jay was, we discovered, bisexual. What's more, he used butyl nitrite only when he was with a homosexual lover. "It gives me a terrific feeling—as if I'm having an orgasm. But I can go on and on, repeating the experience again and again."

We tested him under the influence of the butyl nitrite and recorded repeated orgasms. Here was an example of a man who was multi-orgasmic but who had to be told that was what was happening before he was willing to believe it. When he saw our graphs and recognized the similarity between his "high" experiences and his final orgasms with ejaculation he was surprised and pleased, admitting at last that he was actually multi-orgasmic. He had never identified his "dry orgasms" for what they were because, like so many men, he believed that orgasm and ejaculation were synonymous.

Since Jay was the only subject we have tested who used butyl nitrite, we can't say what effect it might have on other people. However, amyl nitrite and similar drugs have been reported as having an effect similar to that of butyl nitrite.

We have, however, a strong warning against the use of any such drugs to reach multiple orgasms. Amyl nitrite, for example, causes an instantaneous surge of blood, speeding up the heartbeat to a dangerous level. Several physicians whom we know who have in the past used such drugs during sex now no longer do so.

Paul, a physician friend of ours, reported to us on the use of amyl nitrite. "I noticed that I'd get these terrific headaches afterward. It felt great while I was using it, and I had one orgasm after another, but I decided it was dangerous and not worth it. Now I find I can still go a long time and satisfy my partner."

Ziggy, another doctor friend, reported much the same thing. "I used to use it (amyl nitrite) all the time during lovemaking. But the last time, I got a headache afterward that wouldn't go away. It scared me, and now I won't go near the stuff. My health is too important to me."

Ziggy reports that he still has great sex, and can last for a long time. He worries, sometimes, that he might have done himself permanent damage, even though he no longer has headaches and he's stayed away from the drug for a couple of years. However, he, like Jay, is bisexual, and he occasionally finds himself with a homosexual partner who uses a drug, which stirs up his worries about his own health.

All in all, we have concluded that drugs, though sometimes providing a shortcut to multi-orgasms, are not necessary and are often dangerous. A man who wishes to become multi-orgasmic can do so if he practices the exercises we describe, and if he is determined to reach his goal.

Nationality and Multiple Orgasm

Our multi-orgasmic subjects came from other countries and different cultural groups. Is that important?

We think it is. Some sexual techniques seem tied to cultural conditioning, but multi-orgasmic response is not. Possibly this is because it is a learned skill, usually mastered early in life during masturbation. For some men, the skill is easily transferred to intercourse. Others seem unable to relax enough to reach multi-orgasm with a partner but still do so when they masturbate. But the transfer can be made, just as the skill can be learned, no matter what ethnic background a man may have.

4

For Some, It's Natural

In the fifteen years of her work as a sex therapist, Mrs. Fithian has taken well over a thousand sex histories of functional and dysfunctional men, each one lasting from three to seven hours. Briefer histories of several thousand men have been taken during consultation by Dr. Hartman. In addition, many of the male research subjects have been interviewed extensively and their sex histories taken.

In all of these interviews, certain common factors appear. By far most of the men learned about sex when young, through contact with friends who often knew no more than they did. Also, the majority of the men interviewed said they didn't know what to expect. They had not been told about erections and/or orgasms by parents or companions, so that in most cases, they were frightened by their first sexual experiences.

Scared by the Power of Sex

Steve's story is typical. He was put to bed at the same time every night, whether he was sleepy or not. So, when he didn't feel like sleeping, he'd masturbate. At first, his inexperienced "playing with himself" helped him go to sleep. But then, one night, everything changed.

"I was awake longer than usual, and as I played with myself, my penis began to swell up. I didn't know what was happening, but it did feel good, so even though I was a bit frightened, I kept it up for quite a while."

He never told any of his friends, partly because he was naturally shy, and partly because his family moved a lot, and he never felt very close to any boys his own age. "No one ever told me anything," he reports. "And though I did it again, occasionally, I didn't really know what was happening."

Then, when he was about twelve, "I ejaculated. I was really scared. I got it all over the sheets, and I can't remember what frightened me more, my fear that I had hurt myself some way or my fear of what Mom would say about the mess I'd made.

I didn't quit, even though I was scared. I figured I was already doomed, and it felt too good for me to never do it again. But after that I was more careful. I used a pillowcase the second time I ejaculated, and stuffed it down near the bottom of the laundry. I wonder now what Mom thought about all those pillowcases, but she never said anything to me about them."

In spite of his mother's evident tolerance of his act, he still was sure she would not approve of what he was doing. "I really felt guilty about it. It's strange, because no one ever told me it was bad. But, then, no one ever said it was good, either."

John, another subject, said he began masturbating when he was five. "It always felt terrific. But I still was sure it was wrong, somehow. I remember I used to do it under the covers, where no one would see."

Then, when he was about twelve, he was "doing my usual thing when, all of a sudden, this stuff spurted out and it felt all wet." He was scared, turned on the light, and tried to decide what had happened. "I was certain that I was leaking my insides out, and that I was going to die." But there was no blood, and he could see that he hadn't urinated, so he decided to say nothing to anyone. However, he avoided masturbation for some time after that, convinced that what had happened was not good, even though it had felt fine. "I finally overheard a friend talking about masturbating, and I realized then that ejaculation was normal. So I again dared to do it. But I suppose I never quite recovered from my fright and the anxiety I felt about it. And I was always careful to keep from messing my bed again."

Sean, on the other hand, heard about ejaculation when he was very young. His erections began when he was eight, and he learned from his older friends what he could expect. "I used to worry a lot. Not because I ejaculated, but because I didn't. I never quite understood that it was quite normal for a boy of eight to have erections, but that he wouldn't ejaculate until he was close to twelve. Even without ejaculation, I had some wonderful experiences."

We know now that children under the age where ejaculation takes place often have multi-orgasmic experiences, which they enjoy very much. However, when they reach puberty and ejaculation takes place it is such a startling experience that they never again feel that their pre-ejaculation orgasms were very important.

Biologically, this is true. Certainly, a man must ejaculate if he is going to eject sperm and sire a child. But we aren't speaking of biology—or of the conditions needed for reproduction. We're speaking now of orgasm only. A peak sexual experience. And each time we have the chance to interview a man about his childhood sexual experiments, we find the same thing. He describes, in retrospect, what appears to be nonejaculatory orgasms—exactly what is needed if a man is to have repeated orgasms without tiring. What these men learned either from us or through experimenting on their own is that both kinds of orgasms are still possible.

A man who learns the technique for having multiple orgasms can decide each time he has a sexual experience what he wants for himself and for his partner.

Different Cultures—Different Expectations

In the United States, we think of a fifteen-year-old as a child. This approach is not reflected in many parts of the modern world. There are still places where a fifteen-year-old is considered a man, capable of marrying, siring children, and providing for his family. In the current Iran-Iraq war "men" in their early teens are sent into battle. In some countries boys are considered men as soon as they can ejaculate (sire children).

Let's not be too quick to condemn this view. In the early American colonies, a youth often went to work when he was nine or ten, married at fifteen (or even younger), and set up his own, independent household with a bride close to his own age, or a bit older. Life expectancy was short, not much more than twenty-five to thirty years, and so reproduction had to start early if a man was to care for his children until they could be on their own.

Each year since then, with improvements in medical care and nutrition, life expectancy has increased for both men and women. The age for starting work, for assuming family responsibilities—for accepting an adult role in society—was pushed back, first to late teens, and now into early or mid-twenties. But physically our bodies haven't altered to fit our new circumstances. "Children" of twelve are still capable of having children. Maybe, in some future time, nature will adapt to this alteration in society. Maybe then girls and boys will not mature physically until their twenties. But so far there has been no indication of such a change taking place. Girls, in fact, mature earlier now than they did in the past, since they generally have far better nutrition than their grandmothers did.

This lag between physical and social maturity has created many problems. Once, for example, religious groups encouraged early marriage, both to comply with God's decree that they "increase and multiply," and because of St. Paul's admonition that "It is better to marry than to burn." Now, more and more religious groups recognize the need for population control, and many are accepting birth control as essential to a stable society. Although there are churches still strongly opposed to abortion, the trend toward birth control still exists.

Even in rural areas of America, where in the past large families were common, there's been a definite drop in family size. The reason is obvious. In the past, farm children were farmhands. Now machinery has supplanted child labor, and production has increased. Children have lost their value as cheap labor. So farmers, like their city brothers, have small families. In most Western countries, sex, if it is to be indulged in at all, must be enjoyed as a pleasure—with any possibility of conception carefully avoided. Children, when they come, are "wanted," not accidents. The old religion-based idea that sex must be indulged in only for the purpose of having children is no longer accepted by many people, both in and out of the church.

This change in outlook toward sex is spreading around the world, as one country after another becomes aware of the hazards of overpopulation. A country moving from primitive culture into a "modern" mechanized society may adopt birth control, abortion, or sometimes even consider homosexuality as a viable way of avoiding too high a birth rate.

We can see the change in our acceptance of what, in the past, was considered pornographic. Books on pleasurable sex are common today. A few years ago, they would have been banned as obscene. The current trend toward renting and buying X-rated movies by couples and singles for viewing in the privacy of their own homes is further indication of acceptance of material formerly seen as pornographic.

The first result of this awareness of sex as a pleasurable recreation appeared about twenty years ago with an increased emphasis on the woman's enjoyment of the sex act. Now we have come full circle. True, a woman needs to enjoy sex. No one today would consider advocating that she should return to the old idea that sex is something a man does and a woman endures.

But neither should a woman be the only one to enjoy extended sex. One of the side effects of sex for pleasure is a growing awareness that men, too, need to receive more than a momentary surge of pleasure from sex play, if it is to be continued for any length of time.

How Does This Affect You—and Your Partner?

Like an earthquake, according to one woman. She could barely contain her enthusiasm when she talked to us.

"Hey, it's great! Before, Jack hardly got in me before he came. Now he goes long enough for me to really have a good one. It's nice for me—and for him, too. I don't feel so nervous about him anymore. I was always afraid he'd come and end everything. Now, if he does come as we're really in it, it doesn't change things, and if I feel him coming—you know, his penis kind of jerks—it turns me on more. I really dig it."

Shari, another client at our sex clinic, had listened to everything we told her and Terry, her husband, about "dry" orgasms, and their importance in developing multi-orgasmic response in a man. She was ecstatic the first time Terry had an orgasm without ejaculating.

It happened while they were practicing the nondemand

pleasuring exercise that is part of our treatment. She was using the squeeze technique to help him delay his orgasm. For them, this was the most important part of their therapy. Their otherwise happy marriage was threatened by his inability to "hold off" long enough for her to come during intercourse.

They were six days into a two-week intensive therapy program, and had been assigned, as part of their daily exercises, to practice nondemand pleasuring. "What happened," Terry explained, "is that I was turned on by the body caressing and the quiet vagina, and I was ready to ejaculate when we started doing the pleasuring, nondemand thing. Then something strange happened. She had to squeeze me about every minute for seven or eight minutes, and I thought I'd lost it. You know, I waited too long for her to begin the squeezing." (The "quiet vagina" is practiced by inserting the penis in the vagina and then remaining completely still until the man's erection subsides. Sometimes this nonmoving form of intercourse can be continued for a long time with neither ejaculation nor loss of erection occurring.)

He had violent contractions of the pelvic muscles but he didn't ejaculate. "Not at all. I kept my full erection, and then we went on for eleven more minutes without any problem. It was great. I've never been able to take that much handling before without coming. But this time I built up again, and I had all those nice feelings of orgasm, but I didn't come then, either. I didn't ejaculate at all."

We talked about the difference between an orgasm with ejaculation and one without, and of the importance of separating the two kinds of orgasms in one's mind. Shari and Terry agreed that what he had experienced was both new to him and very exciting.

"It was just like when he really comes," Shari explained. "But he didn't fade away, like he used to. And I had a breakthrough, too. I had a little orgasm, with him inside me. I've never had that happen before. He always quit too soon." She rated her "little orgasm" at about four on a scale of ten. Not great, certainly—but a good beginning. As they continued their practice, her response improved. He took great pleasure in his ability to have "dry" orgasms, which let him continue until she had orgasms, too. By the time their therapy was ended, she was having strong orgasms during intercourse.

There is one important point regarding Terry's problem with coming quickly. Like most men, he assumed that the only acceptable way to perform coitus was to thrust violently as soon as he entered. During therapy, and while practicing the nondemand pleasuring technique, he learned to move more slowly, allowing his excitement to build up over a longer period of time. This technique intensifies the pleasure a man has in intercourse, and gives his partner time to build up to orgasm.

It would seem, certainly, that anything that can enhance and enrich a relationship, especially if it is easily accomplished and makes sex more pleasurable, is worth the time and effort it takes to learn. Strangely enough, it is sometimes the woman who is so set in her idea of a man's role in intercourse that she makes it impossible for him to use his ability to have multiple orgasms during intercourse.

Jack, another subject of ours, talked to us at length about his multi-orgasmic pattern. When we asked him if it ever occurred when he had intercourse, he shook his head. "The women I date don't seem to like me to continue once I have an orgasm. Once I kept on after my first orgasm, and my partner got all bent out of shape. She made it clear she thought I was weird. Men just didn't behave that way. So I don't do it with partners anymore. Only when I masturbate."

He admitted that all this might change if he settled on one steady relationship. "Then I could talk it all out with her, so she'd understand."

Possibly this attitude on the part of Jack's female partners was due to their age. Jack was in his early twenties, and the women he dated were younger. Most of them knew little about sex, other than "how to do it." All of them seemed to have definite ideas about what was going to happen. Variations from the expected seemed to frighten them.

Are Swingers Masters of Multiple Orgasms?

Early in our research, we developed contacts with a number of swingers (sometimes called "mate-swappers"), visiting with them during their "parties," and even speaking to groups of swingers on invitation. We had some expectations of our own regarding the groups as a whole. We assumed that most women swingers would be multi-orgasmic, and that the men would also be skilled at the techniques needed to extend sexual pleasure.

To our surprise, we found that our expectations were not reflected in fact. The common statement was "As soon as Harry shoots his wad, he's finished." The women, too, generally had not experienced multiple orgasms. Most participants in swinging rested between encounters until they felt stimulated by some new partner to "go at it" again.

This has changed in recent years. Now more women and men are reporting multi-orgasmic responses, either their own or a partner's.

We recently conducted research on an older subject and his fifty-five-year-old partner. Both were swingers who enjoyed sex a great deal. Both were married to spouses who showed no interest in sex. Incidentally, both felt that their marriages were basically good, and didn't want them threatened by indiscriminate "sleeping around." Swinging, for them, was the solution.

These two met at a swinging party and found that they enjoyed the same kind of slow, multi-orgasmic sex. They soon decided that the parties were unnecessary. Instead, they began to meet at motels, where they could enjoy sex undisturbed. And, somewhere along the way, they heard of our research and decided it might be "fun" to let us test them.

Their typical pattern was to meet first at a motel for a three-to-four-hour session, and then come to the Center for further intercourse, with our nine-channel monitoring devices connected. They were ideal subjects. They functioned with limited movement, which simplified the attachment of our devices, and they were willing to talk to us during their testing, telling us what was "going on" with them. They came to us for monitoring about half-a-dozen times.

5

It Takes Practice—and Exercise

Every day. Once you start a program aimed at your becoming multi-orgasmic, you'll be doing pelvic exercises and contractions every day. It's easy to understand why this is necessary. There are several muscle groups in the pelvis. If all of them are used, you can stop the flow of urine, even if it is strong.

Separately, each set of muscles has a slightly different function. The levator ani muscle is the one that you tighten to stop the flow of urine. In people who are out of shape physically, this muscle often weakens, resulting in poor bladder control. But a weak levator ani muscle can also result in constipation. We recommend exercises of this muscle to improve sexual control. As the muscle grows stronger, erections come more easily, and sexual endurance increases. There are also obvious beneficial side effects that come to a person who follows our regimen. When the "pelvic floor" has been strengthened, bladder and bowel control improves. Good "pelvic health" contributes to better over-all well-being.

A man wishing to maintain good pelvic health needs to contract his PC muscle about fifty times every day. If he wishes to become multi-orgasmic, he will have to repeat the contraction of this muscle at least a hundred times every day.

One thing to remember: You are going to be exercising a group of muscles. Like any other muscle, they tire quickest when weak. So don't try to start with a hundred contractions the first time you exercise. Begin with a small number, quitting before you tire. Then gradually build up the amount, always being ready to "back off" a bit if you find your muscles getting sore.

Don't let this warning discourage you. Most people who begin this series of exercises find that they can maintain a hundred contractions a day after only a short buildup of less than a week.

For a drawing of the pelvic muscles that will help you to understand the exercise, see page 165. If you understand just where the muscles are located and what they do, you will find it easier to exercise effectively.

Can you be sure this will help you? Two examples of clients who gained by exercising their pelvic muscles are Clint and Verne.

Clint came to us because his wife, Beth, refused to have sex with him. "She says there's so much secretion before I even come that it bothers her. She won't even kiss me there anymore, because she says she gets all wet."

When we assured him that there might be nothing abnormal in his abundance of precoital fluid, he seemed upset. "You've got to help me. My wife is beautiful, and I love her. We've only been married a few months, and my marriage is going down the tubes."

Usually severely weakened pelvic muscles do not appear in a young man who is in top physical condition, so we again warned Clint that there might nothing we could do to help him. But he persisted. He was, obviously, willing to try almost anything to cure himself of what he considered a terrible problem. We suggested then that he begin with fifty contractions of the pelvic muscles every day for the first week, and build up to a hundred each day by the second week.

Fortunately, these muscles are easy to identify. We told him to try, the next time he urinated, to stop the flow. The muscles he used to do this are the very muscles that are to be exercised for sexual control. Clint went home and followed our directions. Two weeks later, when he reported back, he was in far better spirits. His overabundant precoital fluid was under control at last, and his wife was once more willing to accept his sexual advances.

We had no way of knowing whether there had actually been any change in the amount of precoital fluid. The entire problem might have been caused by lack of knowledge. This is, in fact, a major problem. People are often so misinformed or uninformed sexually that they assume that what is happening to them is "abnormal," when it is, in fact, quite common. For such people, just providing correct information regarding their own body functions often solves their problems. (See page 166 for a comment on this particular type of case.)

Verne came in for a different reason. He had a slight loss of urine that had resulted in visits to doctors during most of his life. He had been a bedwetter as a child, and he never really gained control over his pelvic muscles. Even as an adult, he had often suffered embarrassing "accidents."

We suggested that he do fifty pelvic contractions every day as a beginning. He did more, however, and in three days he was no longer "leaking," as he described it.

"All my life I've had problems," he explained. "It feels great to go to the bathroom and not find urine on my underpants."

Now that the problem seemed to be cured, he explained that he had never dated because he was so sure he had an unpleasant odor. "I've changed my underpants as often as three times a day, but I still felt that I smelled."

In Verne's case, we solved his "leaking" problem as well

as improved his sex life. He was thirty-four years old, and a virgin at the time he visited us. However, by the end of his two-week therapy, he had no problem with accidental urination. He was able to go several hours without having to find a restroom, and the extra changes of shorts were a thing of the past. With that goal reached, he dared to date women he had avoided before.

Now It's Your Turn to Exercise

A word of warning: It is best if you scatter your pelvic exercises throughout the day, rather than trying to do a hundred all at once. This way the muscles will build up without tiring.

And one of encouragement: These pelvic exercises can be done any time—on the bus or in your car, at your desk, or as you sit waiting in the dentist's office. You can even do them as you walk.

To identify the "right" muscles, do what we told Clint to do: urinate. While the flow is full, try to close it off. The muscles you will automatically tighten in this attempt are the ones you must exercise. And how do you exercise them? By tightening them—as if you were trying to close off the flow of urine. If you remember to tighten and relax these muscles off and on during the day, you will easily build up to a hundred contractions.

We recommend that you begin by selecting certain key activities as reminders that you must exercise. Begin by always contracting the pelvic muscle as you ride to and from work and as you answer the phone. If you keep this up for a day or two, you will develop a habit that will stay with you. Soon you will always exercise the pelvic muscles whenever you are in a car or talking on the phone.

As with all other motor activities, these exercises will soon become automatic. You won't even realize you're doing them, even though at first you had to think about them to do them right. It's just like braking, shifting gears, or staying in your lane when you're on the highway. When you first learned to drive, each one of those actions required concentrated thought. Now, if you've been driving for any length of time, you do them without thinking.

One bit of advice: There are actually two kinds of exercises. In the first, you tighten the muscles, hold them tense for the count of three seconds, and then relax them. We suggest that you do this exercise about twenty-five times a day at first, in groups of five, spaced throughout the day.

In the second, you tighten and relax quickly, as you would during orgasm. Begin by doing this one twenty-five times a day, too, in groups of five each, also spacing it through the day.

As your muscles grow stronger, you should increase the total number of contractions of both kinds, keeping them equally balanced. You will find that soon you are able to prolong intercourse simply by contracting these muscles just before what is called "ejaculatory inevitability" takes place.

This is the moment just before any semen actually moves into the urethra, but when you are beginning to feel that you will soon "come." Don't get discouraged if you don't immediately achieve this goal. Your muscles must be very strong to control this "natural" occurrence. After all, if you decided to become a long-distance runner, you would hardly expect to run a marathon after a week of practice, would you? So be patient with yourself. And don't give up. Your success depends on how faithful you are in exercising and on how many exercises you do every day. Certainly that shouldn't be a surprise to anyone.

We've found that it helps if you keep a record of your exercise activities. In the Appendix on page 169 we have a chart you can use, or you can make up your own. Some men simply mark the number of contractions they do in a corner of each square of a weekly calendar. It makes little difference how you keep track of your progress, but we strongly urge that you use some record as a reminder of how close you are to reaching your goal.

Incidentally, this use of pelvic muscle exercises to help solve problems of premature ejaculation was mentioned in *Sexology* magazine as early as 1958. The difficulty was that the exercises were not described carefully, or presented in any systematic manner. Nor were there any suggestions as to the number of contractions that were desirable.

With the advance in understanding of sexual physiology, the importance of these muscles to good pelvic health is now accepted. Twenty-five years after they were first recognized as having value in improving sexual function, the pelvic muscles are at last receiving the attention they deserve.

Get that Circulation Going

We hear a lot these days about the build-up of fat in the arteries. We know it can lead to heart problems and strokes. What many people don't realize is that a build-up of fat in the blood vessels of the pelvic area causes poor circulation, and that can affect sexual response. To put it bluntly, a man with this problem will have difficulty getting an erection.

If he's lucky, he'll just have to get used to waiting longer before he's "hard." If the circulation problem is more severe, he may never get a full erection, no matter how much he is stimulated. Obviously, the most important part of the cure for this condition is an improved diet and medical care designed to reduce the fat particles in the blood. But we've found that the pelvic exercises we advocate also help.

What do they do? First of all, as the muscles of the pelvis are exercised, blood is forced through the capillaries. This stronger flow of blood starts a "clean-up" process, "washing" the fat away. With more room, the blood flows even more quickly and the clean-up continues. The second thing that happens is that the pelvic muscles become more flexible. You might compare a well-toned pelvic muscle to a new rubber band and a "flabby" one to a worn-out rubber band. When a muscle loses its tone, the entire body is affected.

The pelvic muscles support the entire body, like the foundation of a tall building. If they are weak, the entire structure of the body is harmed. If you bring them back into condition through exercise, the entire body benefits. Even the prostate gland, an organ that often suffers as a man ages, can benefit from improved tone in the pelvic muscles. Consider that the muscles that surround the prostate gland contract during orgasm—or would contract if they were as strong as they should be. As you strengthen the pelvic muscles, you will help the prostate gland return to the function for which it was designed.

It's possible that many prostate problems are caused not by actual damage to the prostate, but by weakening of the muscles that surround it. We know that a man who has sex two or three times a week usually has little or no prostate problems. That's because, with regular orgasms, the pelvic muscles contract often and stay in good condition.

Many men, as they grow older, have sex less and less often. The effect is like a chain reaction. Less sex means fewer orgasms. That means the muscles in the lower pelvic region remain idle—and grow flabby. If, on the contrary, the pelvic muscles are regularly used, either in intercourse, masturbation, or while doing PC exercises, they stay in good condition, and the whole body benefits.

Many of our clients and research subjects report on the good aspects of the exercises. Doug, a client, reported: "I always thought I had great erections. But since I've been doing the PC exercises, my penis gets harder—and bigger—than it ever did before. Maybe I'm just more aware now than I used to be—but I don't think that's it."

Brad, a research subject, was impressed with the effect of his exercises on his orgasms. "I always have had fantastic orgasms. But what's happening to me now is crazy. I build and build, and when I come, it's like I'm going to explode!"

So if you've assumed that people with weak muscle structure are the only people who get returns from a regular exercise program for the pelvic muscles, think again. Even if you aren't yet convinced that men can have multiple orgasms, there are some very good reasons for your starting the exercises. And if you suddenly find yourself capable of extended sex play, you've received an extra bonus.

This point must be made at the start. The pelvic exercises should be done consistently. We've already told you how to recognize what must be done. Begin by trying to stop your urine flow. If you can't do it, no matter how hard you try, then you have proof of how weak your PC muscle actually is. But don't despair. As you practice, the muscle will strengthen. So, as a test, we recommend that you periodically repeat the stop urine test. You should show a gradual improvement if you're doing the exercises correctly.

Don't just exercise when you urinate, however. We've already mentioned that no one else need know that you're doing your exercises, so just do them—regularly.

Incidentally, any boy with a flair for experimentation can tell you that when he tenses the muscle in his crotch his penis moves. That shouldn't surprise you. The same muscle used to have the job of wagging the tail, back when we walked on all fours. Then it had an easy task. Things are harder for the PC muscle now, because we stand on our hind legs and throw the muscle out of normal position. But it still does the job. It just has to work harder. And for that, it has to be strong.

You Need a Schedule

Any bodybuilder will tell you that the easiest way to maintain an effective exercise schedule is to tie it in with something you do frequently. We've mentioned doing the exercises in your car. If you travel a lot in your business, that's a good place to start. But if you're desk-bound, making phone calls all day, knock off a few exercises each time you pick up the phone. By the end of the day you'll have met —or exceeded—your planned schedule. Just remember how it goes: Tighten, hold for the count of three—relax. Or do a number of quick tighten-relax ones. They're both important.

For starters, don't overdo. We suggest beginning with ten in the morning, before you get out of bed. Follow that with ten "flicking" exercises. Remember, that's when you tighten and release quickly, over and over again. Your goal for first-of-the-morning exercises is to do twenty of each without feeling too tired.

Why do any of these exercises when you're lying down? That's an easy one to answer. It lets the muscles work without any pressure on them from the weight of the organs in the pelvic cavity.

The next time when you might regularly do another set of the exercises is at lunch. No one will ever know. You might do three of each every time you urinate. That will add a few more repeats by the end of the day. And then, before you go to sleep at night, go through the routine ten more times. With a good foundation like that, you'll find it easy to add a few more to each session. In no time, you'll be doing fifty a day. And you'll build to one hundred without any feeling that you're taxing yourself.

A word of warning: If your pelvic muscles feel sore at all, cut back on the number you do until you've worked through the discomfort. That's what you'd do were your legs to get sore from jogging, or your arms and back from weightlifting. Just don't panic. Some men do when they have any discomfort in the genitalia. Such a man seems very afraid that he'll lose all ability to get erections, or that something terrible is happening to his penis. But nothing is going wrong. Of course, if pain persists it might have no relationship to the exercises you're doing. In that case, a visit to a doctor is in order. Under normal conditions it is safe to treat the pelvic muscles as you do any other muscles in your body; don't worry about the natural reaction that results from too much exercise all at once.

Your final goal is to do about two hundred exercises a day. It sounds formidable, but you can already see that it isn't. Most of your exercising can be accomplished while you're doing something else, so you'll hardly notice the time you spend on it.

It's important for you to understand that the penis itself is not a muscle, nor does it have any muscles in it. If you look in the Appendix, you'll see a drawing of the penis showing flaccid and erect stages that will explain how erection occurs. It will also help you understand why the pelvic exercises can help erections.

Incidentally, these exercises are very good for impotent men, since they do increase the blood flow to the penis. According to Dr. Arnold Milman, 22 million men have impotence problems. We're convinced that some of those men would benefit from a regular pelvic exercise program, masturbation, or a combination of both. Many of our clients come to us with erection problems caused by lack of sexual stimulation or inadequate sexual activity, and, of those, 50 percent or more are helped by this simple prescription.

It might surprise you to learn that many women prefer a penis that, though erect, is not stone hard. Why? Because the tissues in the vagina can be delicate, and when it is penetrated by a rock-hard penis a woman may feel discomfort. An erect but flexible penis is less apt to hurt. What we term a "50 percent erection" is certainly adequate for penetration and thrusting.

There are, of course, other types of impotence than that caused by lack of exercise. They won't be helped by our regimen. Psychogenic impotence (impotence caused by fear, tension, or anxiety), as well as impotence caused by medication or illness can't go away just because you exercise a few muscles. But such causes are far rarer than most men think. If you're having erection problems because you don't have sex very often, or because you've grown flabby, you'll see improvement very soon after you start.

Ted, who was fifty-two, came to us because he'd met a ". . . lucious gal, twenty-five, who likes me. We've gone out twice, and gone to bed both times. But I didn't get an erection either time." He expressed surprise that she was still willing to give him another chance, and he didn't want to flub again. He gave us a deadline. They were going to Palm Springs together—in three weeks.

He presented us with quite a problem. His wife was dead, but she had been ill for several years before she died, and in that time he had not masturbated nor had sex with any other woman. What's more, since her death, two years before he came to see us, he had had no interest in sex or dating.

We warned him that we might not be able to help in that short a time. Usually we allow six visits, each a week apart, before we consider the training complete. We told him that he had to work daily at the exercises and masturbate at least two or three times a week.

That bit of instruction almost sent him away. He declared that masturbation was "kid stuff," and that he was too old for such nonsense. But, in spite of his objections, he thought we were his only hope.

He was consistent in following the exercise regimen, especially when we convinced him that it really was up to him to improve his ability to function—that we could only advise.

He went on his weekend after only three sessions with us. The following Monday, he phoned. "I'm not coming back. Don't need to. We screwed our heads off." They had sex on Friday night after they arrived at the hotel, three times on Saturday, and twice on Sunday before they headed for home. He sounded "high" from the experience. "I just called to thank you," he added before he ended the call.

Of course, he did it all. He was motivated, and conscientious about doing his exercises. He had masturbated every day during the three weeks and had worked up to five hundred pelvic contractions every day. He had also had a couple of counseling appointments where he had learned more facts about human sexual functioning. This helped him to feel more relaxed and less apprehensive about the weekend that meant so much to him.

He went to Palm Springs with his body in reasonable physical condition, with pelvic muscles that were accustomed to use (after some years of inactivity), and with a relaxed attitude based on knowledge. His fears of failure were gone. Undoubtedly, he could have benefited from more treatment. But he had accomplished what he wanted to achieve, and he was happy with the results.

This, incidentally, is one of the advantages of this specific set of exercises. You can do them until you reach whatever goal you set for yourself. But you have to do them. It's like dieting. We can give you all kinds of advice, but unless you act on it, nothing will change for you.

6

The Solitary Player

It's a touchy subject. We all remember what our parents used to say about masturbation. Even adults who consider themselves free from childhood conditioning often shy away from open discussion of what *Webster's Dictionary* defines as "erotic stimulation of the genital organs commonly resulting in orgasm and achieved by manual or other bodily contact exclusive of sexual intercourse, by instrumental manipulation, occasionally by sexual fantasies, or by various combinations of these agencies."

Kinsey has, for years, been the authority on sex, even in the minds of those who have never read his works. According to him, masturbation is "any sort of self stimulation which brings erotic arousal." In addition, he defines masturbation as: "deliberate self stimulation."

Many readers of his writing might feel that by using the word *deliberate,* he was condemning masturbation. "Deliberate" indeed! If it's deliberate, the assumption is that it must be bad! What's unfortunate about this assumption on the part of any reader is that Kinsey was a scientist. He described and studied. He did not judge.

Ministers have a more judgmental attitude toward the act, though their definitions are similar to Kinsey's and *Webster's*. Summed up, they consider masturbation manual self-stimulation for a pleasurable purpose. Which purpose, when pressed, they admit is "ejaculation." They seemed to find it difficult to separate the act from their concept of it as "spilling of seed," which they claim is directly forbidden in the Bible. Even ministers who do not oppose contraception seemed opposed to masturbation.

When we pointed out the inconsistency of their attitude, they replied that "contraception isn't 100 percent effective. There still is a chance that conception can occur. But to just waste the seed—that isn't right."

We find this an interesting dichotomy. The biblical story of Onan, on which the prohibition against masturbation is based, seems to us to have other overtones.

Onan was expected to impregnate his dead brother's wife, since his brother had died without having a son. At the time, this was common cultural practice, since the high death rate (pestilence, wars, infant mortality) made every birth an important event. For his own reasons, Onan withdrew during intercourse and "spilled his seed on the ground."

For this sin, God put him to death. Why? Maybe because he refused to obey an order. Maybe because he "argued" with God. Maybe because he wanted his sons by his own wife, rather than the son he might give his older brother's wife, to be inheritors of his father's lands and fortune. Or maybe because he felt loyalty to his wife and didn't want to "spread his seed," even if it was culturally acceptable.

But times have changed. Today we have problems of over—not under—population. We are constantly being warned by ecologists and scientists studying population growth that we must cut down on the birthrate if we are to save the earth from destruction. Yet, with this new set of values, there are still many people who cling to the old rules. We are taught that masturbation is "bad," and that the best role for a woman is motherhood.

But we are, fortunately, rational people. We can change our attitudes once we recognize that these prohibitions against masturbation are not applicable today. Unfortunately, that doesn't make them any less real to those who accept them. Sex therapists must deal with the feelings a person has about masturbation before they can use masturbation as a form of therapy.

Are We Alone?

Fortunately, we aren't. In 1972, the American Medical Association published a book called *Human Sexuality.* In it were several references to masturbation, all of them favorable. "Masturbation," one statement said, "is a normal part of adolescent sexual development and requires no medical management."

In another place the reference was even more permissive. "Masturbation is practiced by men and women of all ages, often as a supplement to marital coitus, and women tend to masturbate more often as they grow older."

Irwin Marcus, M.D., a psychoanalyst, remarked that "Refuting the misconceptions about masturbation that have been handed down over thousands of years, modern researchers have found that it can hardly be considered a rare, unusual, or abnormal human activity."

Bernie Zilbergeld, Ph.D., in his book *Male Sexuality,* includes an entire chapter on masturbation. What's more, he defends this act in the following way: "First it is one of the best ways of enhancing your sexuality and overcoming any sexual difficulties you may be experiencing. This is especially true for men without partners. Second, masturbation as practiced by many men is not as pleasurable as it might be and, moreover, is accompanied by feelings of guilt or shame. Overcoming some of these negative feelings enables you better to enjoy your autoerotic practices."

Jack Annon, Ph.D., in his two-volume work *The Behavioral Treatment of Sexual Problems,* also notes the importance of masturbation in resolving sexual problems.

So we're not alone. Not at all. Most serious sex researchers agree that masturbation, far from being harmful, is actually one of the most valuable tools available for treating sexual problems. If you want to read more about what these and other researchers have said, read Chapter Fourteen.

So It's Normal to Masturbate, Is It?

Yes, it is. Perfectly normal. And Kinsey was right. Almost every American boy masturbates at some time or another before he matures.

To refresh you as to what Kinsey actually learned, here are a few statistics. He found that 95 percent of all American men who had a high school education had masturbated by the time they reached twenty-one. The figure for men who attended college was a bit higher. He was talking about "deliberate self stimulation," not accidental hand-genital contact such as scratching. So the question of whether it is "good" or "bad" is moot. The fact remains that masturbation is practiced commonly by most males.

So what's the point of feeling guilty about it? There are so many reasons for masturbating, all of them valid. Some men masturbate just for the pleasure it gives them. Others do it to relieve tension, and not necessarily sexual tension, either. Some use masturbation only when they have no partner available, and others use masturbation to maintain their multi-orgasmic abilities or just to keep their sex functions operating, even when they have regular partners.

Furthermore, men masturbate in different ways. A man accustomed to the idea that orgasm and ejaculation are synonymous will masturbate until he has an orgasm. One orgasm. Then he's through. A man who is multi-orgasmic will be accustomed to continuing his coital activity for a longer time, and so he'll use the same techniques when he masturbates that work when he has sex with a partner. If you want to become multi-orgasmic, you need to learn to do what these men do.

Are we saying what you think we are?

Absolutely! If you want to become multi-orgasmic, use masturbation as the most direct route to learning this new skill.

Is there a danger that you'll become addicted to masturbation? Not if you weren't before.

Do you consider masturbation "kid stuff?" So do a number of our clients, but when they realize how valuable it can be as a learning tool, they are glad they ignored their first reaction.

Let's analyze this once more. What is the major difference between a multi-orgasmic and a single-orgasmic man?

Nothing physical. Multi-orgasmic men aren't bigger, thinner, fatter, younger, or stronger than men who have single orgasms. The only difference is that a multi-orgasmic man continues his coital activities longer than a man who is singly-orgasmic.

That's what you're going to work toward. The ability to last—and therefore to enjoy sex (coitus)—for a longer period than you do now. It's as simple as that. Through the use of masturbation, you're going to learn to have a number of "dry" orgasms without losing your erection. This will most likely be a gradual process.

Another point to remember. You'll establish a pattern when you have multiple orgasms during masturbation. Some men find that their first orgasm comes very quickly (within a minute) after they begin to masturbate. If you are like that, don't worry that this will not fit with your partner's pattern when you share sex with her. All the men we have worked with easily learned how to go longer.

You Already Know How to Masturbate?
Don't Be So Sure!

Who taught you how to masturbate?

No one?

Then how did you learn?

There's not much chance that it was a subject that appeared in your college curriculum. Certainly you never had a lesson on masturbation in high school or in the fifth-grade health class.

Oh, you just "kind of picked it up," when you were a kid? You did what felt good, and kept it up? Like the men we talked about earlier in this book?

That's certainly a lot better than not learning at all. But there are certain skills that would make your masturbation more effective. That's what you'll learn here.

We are convinced that masturbation has an important role in every person's life, whether married or not. And this is why.

It all comes back to a discussion of sex in general. What is sex, after all? What are we saying to a partner when we have intercourse?

Oh, you tell her you think she's beautiful. You say you love her. Sounds great. But is that what your actions are saying?

Jeannie, a client of ours, was very open about her reactions to the reason for much of the sex she had with her husband. "I love to have intercourse with Joe—most of the time. I know he loves me, and it's a wonderful way of showing it. But there are times . . ."

Joe looked surprised. This was one of our "together sessions," when some of the problems a couple faces are talked out.

Jeannie continued, not looking at her husband. "When he uses me to get rid of the tensions from his job, I've had it. I feel used . . ." her voice dropped, ". . . and abused."

We could see that Joe was still in shock. So we concentrated on Jeannie. "How would you feel about him masturbating at a time like that?"

"I wish he would." Jeannie looked up now, directly at Joe. "He's ruining our relationship."

Now we turned to Joe. "How do you feel about masturbating?"

He grimaced. "Well." He snorted. "I got married so I wouldn't have to do that anymore."

"You heard what Jeannie said. She feels you're ruining the relationship by having sex whenever you want to, without any concern for how she feels about it." We turned back to Jeannie. "Is that right?"

She nodded.

Joe's voice was stronger this time. "It's her duty."

We ignored his remark. "Do you want her to get so fed up she leaves you?"

He looked directly at us this time. "That isn't what she said. And no. Of course I don't want her to leave me. She won't, either. We love each other."

"Then why are you here?" He didn't answer, so we continued. "She insisted that you come. You already told us that. And do you think she'd have made this kind of a fuss if this wasn't important to her? She wants some things changed, doesn't she?"

He mumbled assent.

"We didn't hear Jeannie say she doesn't want to have sex with you. What we heard was that she feels there's a problem that's big enough to cause trouble between you two if it isn't solved. She said you made her feel used and abused. Can you expect that she'll want to stay with you if you keep on using and abusing her?"

Again, the mumbled sound. Was he agreeing?

"What's she's saying is that she wants you to love her —not screw her."

Jeannie came to life. "That's right!" She faced Joe

squarely. "When you come home from work with all your problems, I want you to talk them out with me. But all you do is jack off on me. You aren't even thinking of me at all. It makes me feel bad."

In one form or another, this conversation is repeated often in our consultation room. Closeness in marriage is built with more than just sex. Sex is part of it. An important part, that is true. But a word must be said here for an understanding of the other aspects of a relationship. If a man expects to use intercourse to relieve tension that would better be relieved if he talked a problem out—or masturbated —then he is abusing the act. And he's abusing his wife at the same time.

Sex at its best is an act of love. Keep it that. Use masturbation to relieve tension.

Are we saying, then, that it isn't the responsibility of a wife to meet all of her husband's sex needs?

That's it! Exactly. So what you learn in this book you will probably use many times again, even if you're married, and even if your wife loves you very much. There will be times when you're better off using your hand instead of her.

So now we're back to the same old question: How did most men learn to masturbate? If what we hear is valid at all, most men learn to masturbate as boys, and they learn from other boys. A big boy in the block teaches younger ones. "You move your hand up and down on your prick, and after a while some juice shoots out and it feels good." And that's the extent of the lesson. Orgasms and ejaculation are the same thing. That's what most boys learn.

But we have presented cases where this was not what a boy learned, and they lead us to believe that most of these small boys who listen to their older companion learn something else beside the "right way" to masturbate. They learn to ignore their own experiences. They learn to discount the many times when they continued to "jack off," reaching peak after peak, all without ejaculation. They learn that this experience doesn't count because "that isn't the way it should be done."

Why are we so sure of this? Because, generally speaking, the subjects we studied who continued their multi-orgasmic masturbation into maturity somehow managed to miss the "back alley" lessons in "jacking off" that are so common in our society.

Jim is a good example. As a boy, he learned to masturbate in the shower. He ran water on his penis, and it got hard. When he got old enough, he ejaculated under the shower. He continued this method of masturbating all through high school and college. When he found himself in a gang of boys, talking about masturbation, he could carry his part without ever realizing that they were talking about two different techniques. Jim just never developed a response pattern that was effective when he tried intercourse.

When Jim married, he couldn't get an erection with his partner unless they were in the shower. He had to be taught —as an adult—how to masturbate by copying the up-and-down motion that simulated coitus.

Saul is another man who didn't learn to masturbate by conventional means. He masturbated by lying face down and moving his body so his penis rubbed against the sheet. He, too, had to learn a new pattern of response before he was capable of "normal" sexual intercourse with a partner. His problem? He could get an erection without any difficulty. But coitus did not put enough pressure on his penis, so he couldn't reach a climax.

So you can see that the way a boy learns to masturbate can affect his ability to have intercourse when he becomes a man. If that's so, you can see that how you masturbate now can also affect whether you will eventually be able to have multi-orgasms during coitus. The way you do it *is* important, and we provide specific instructions in Chapter Eight.

7

You're Not Alone When You're Alone

Forgive us for repeating—but this is important.

The first thing you must do is get rid of your fears of masturbating, even if you think you don't have any. They're very deeply ingrained in most men. You've all heard at least one of these old bromides. Remember, they aren't true!

1. Men have only a specific amount of semen. If you waste any by masturbating, you might run out before you're old, and then you'll be impotent. *Nonsense!*

2. You'll get warts on your hands. *Foolishness!*

3. It's sinful. *Wrong!*

4. It's dirty. *Hogwash!*

Masturbation is a natural, normal act, performed by animals as well as humans. There is no cause for guilt. So you have to get rid of the feeling that you're doing something wrong when you touch your genitals. That's important.

Very important.

If you are to learn to be multi-orgasmic, you can't feel guilty while you're doing the exercises. You need to send signals to your brain that say "it's okay, it's really okay," until you truly feel that it is.

Because guilt has a lot to do with the way you have sex.

Guilt Is a Bummer

Guilt often causes men to have sex as if they were late for an appointment. Women know the symptoms. As Mary put it, "It's in, out, and off to sleep. I never have a chance."

There's even an old one-liner about it. "Wham, bam, thank you ma'am."

From the very start, boys aim for quick orgasms. They feel guilty. They know it's wrong. They're afraid they'll be caught.

Dr. Wardell Pomeroy in his book *Boys and Sex* suggests that since most all boys masturbate, they should learn to masturbate for long periods of time so that, as adults, they can "go" longer during intercourse. An excellent suggestion. But there aren't very many parents who encourage their sons' masturbation. Even in a family where masturbation is accepted, there are no lessons given. In fact, since in such families the practice is often to say nothing about it, the results are usually the same as in families where masturbation is considered bad. The child still feels guilty when he does it. Silence isn't always golden.

Bernard was a good example of this "hands off" policy toward self-stimulation. He was "pretty heavily into masturbation" when he was a boy. "I masturbated every day. I'd either go into the bathroom and lock the door, or I'd do it at night—after I went to bed. I was real careful, though. I didn't want to ejaculate in bed, 'cause then my mother would find out. I didn't know how she'd feel about it, but I figured she'd object, and I didn't want to be hassled."

We asked how he avoided messing the bedclothes.

"Well, I used Kleenex—lots of it. And then I had to figure out what to do with all that paper. So most of the time I did it in the shower or in the bathroom, over the toilet. One time I was standing over the toilet masturbating and I'd forgotten to lock the door. My mom came in. She didn't say anything. I was about fourteen, I guess. It really bothered me because she didn't say anything. I was a lot more careful after that."

"Why did it bother you?"

"I guess I thought it was wrong, and that she should have scolded me. I never did quite understand why she never said anything. She didn't even look surprised, and I know she saw me."

"Perhaps she felt it was all right and didn't know you had guilt feelings."

"Maybe. I never thought about it that way. I guess I just figured that anything that feels that good had to be bad." He paused, thinking. "I guess I still feel that way. You know what I mean?"

Yes, we did understand. We've had too many clients who resisted when we tried to get them to masturbate, even when they knew that masturbation would solve the sexual problem that brought them to us.

The truth is that there is tacit acceptance of masturbation among boys. But even today, as enlightened as we are sexually, we still seem to feel that adults shouldn't do it. That they shouldn't need to, especially if they have sex partners.

"Yeah, I masturbated a lot as a kid," Jerry, another client, announced. "But I don't do it now. It isn't right. I'm married. My wife wouldn't like me to. Isn't there anything else I could do? Maybe another woman?"

We had to talk quite a while to convince him that, in our experience with men and women who function well sexually, masturbation is usually engaged in quite frequently. It doesn't take the place of intercourse—but it seems to serve to relieve tension when that is all that is needed, it helps balance things when two people have very different sex drives, it helps one partner when the other is "too tired," uninterested (not necessarily because he or she doesn't love the other, but because of some temporary, all-consuming activity that for a time makes sex secondary), or unavailable. Sometimes such a person masturbates just for fun. Because masturbation still feels good—even when one is an adult.

Can You Overdo It?

A number of people come to us because they fear they are masturbating excessively. Yet when we question them, we find that they are quite normal, especially since most such clients have few opportunities to enjoy intercourse. If a problem exists, it can be because of the location an individual chooses when he masturbates. Obviously, public masturbation will offend others, and could lead to arrest. But the masturbation itself is not the problem.

Rex is a good example of this. Until about five years before he came to us, Rex worked as a stunt driver. His job was filled with tense moments and excitement. When he had an accident that put him in bed for some time, he missed the excitement.

Concurrently, because of the injury he had suffered, he had a lot less sex with his wife. This they both accepted.

But when he regained his health, he and his wife still did not have sex as often as they had before his accident. He came to us because of what he termed "excessive masturbation." He explained that he didn't just masturbate in the bathroom. "If I see a pretty girl when I'm driving along, I'll masturbate in my car. I'm afraid someone will see me. I've even started looking into windows of houses and masturbating while I watch a woman inside. I know that's dangerous. I have to stop it. If I ever got caught, they'd put me away and lose the keys."

He explained that he did this ". . . about two or three times a week. It's too often. I know that. I've got to cut it out."

We know from our research that a man who masturbates two or three times a week is not being excessive, especially if he and his wife have intercourse only every week or two, as Rex and his wife now did. The problem was not how much he masturbated, but his need to combine masturbation with actual danger.

"How does it feel when you're masturbating where you might be caught? Does the adrenalin rush up, and do you feel as turned on as you used to be when you drove a car in some dangerous stunt?"

He seemed surprised at our question, but he nodded yes.

"Do you miss the stunt driving?"

"I sure do. It was a real turn-on. You know." We could see that he was already ahead of us.

"Is there any way you can get some of that excitement back into your life without risking arrest? Have you ever gone to a nudist park?"

"Yes. I liked that, and I didn't feel a need to masturbate while I was there. But my wife hated it, so that's out."

We asked more about his sex life.

"It isn't what it was twenty years ago. We aren't very close anymore, and I miss that. I don't think she cares if we ever have sex."

"Is your behavior a cry for help?" We watched him closely. "Have you ever tried to commit suicide?"

His eyes shot open. "How did you guess that? I did, about five years ago. I was in therapy for three years after that. I wouldn't try that again."

"Not consciously. But have you thought that your risking arrest is a form of suicide? You've told us that it would be the end. That your wife would probably leave you. That you'd have to go to jail and they'd throw away the key. You know they wouldn't do that, of course. But you would have to register as a sex offender, and wherever you moved, you'd have to reregister. If there was ever a sex crime committed, you'd be contacted and questioned. Your life, at least as you know it, would be over."

He was silent for a time. "Yeah, I know. That's why I want you to help me. I don't want that to happen, but I risk it, anyway, don't I?"

Yes, we agreed, he did. We continued. "There's another possibility. Is this, maybe, a way for you to focus attention on yourself—like it was focused on you when you were a stunt driver? Maybe that is part of all this."

Again, he seemed surprised. "How did you know? It does make me feel important. I sort of picture how it would be if I was caught, with a lot of people staring at me. But I know it wouldn't be the same, and I know I'm being stupid. But I just can't stop. That's what scares me."

"Would you ever touch one of the women you watch? Would you hurt anyone?"

He appeared shocked. "Of course not! But my wife thinks I might. And I'm getting a little worried because I feel as if I'm losing control. I do it now even when I tell myself I won't."

"How would you feel about having more contact with your wife, with lots of kissing and hugging?"

He smiled for the first time. "I'd love it! You know, my wife is Catholic, and I know it hurts her when I masturbate. But she won't have sex with me. What am I supposed to do?"

"Have you considered that you might be courting disaster just to get back at her for her rejection?"

He answered quickly. "No, of course not! But if sex was good between us again, I'd probably stop all this."

He decided that he could work on finding something to

do that would give him back at least a bit of the high he used to feel when he drove stunt cars. And he recognized that if he succeeded there, he'd probably lick the problem of his masturbating in dangerous places. His problems were solved in time, but only after he found a substitute for the stunt-car excitement that he missed so much, and developed a closer, more intimate relationship with his wife.

Several other cases of "excessive" masturbation have similar themes. In them, the masturbation was only a side issue. Despite the belief on the part of the client that he was masturbating excessively, he was actually doing it only a couple of times a week.

Only one man in our acquaintance, Jake, could possibly be termed an excessive masturbator. He did it seven to ten times a day—so often that it interfered with his job and with his relationships with others. He wasn't in therapy when we knew him, nor do we know whether he ever sought therapy. What we do know is that the dynamics of his life were similar to those of Rex.

Rex had a wife who worked, who paid little attention to him, and who disapproved of his masturbating. However, he did not have the problem Jake had, since he confined his activity to his own home. In his case, he seemed to get what he wanted. He masturbated this much to get his wife's attention—and he succeeded. After they began to communicate again, his need for therapy vanished.

Occasionally, a couple will come in because the wife complains that her husband prefers masturbation to having sex with her. Sometimes, this is the result of the wife being too demanding of her husband, so that he begins to feel that he can't live up to her expectations. He finally reaches the conclusion that it's easier for him to masturbate than it is for him to try to please her.

You will notice that none of the problems we have mentioned were really problems of masturbation. They were social problems, focusing on masturbation. Sometimes masturbation served as a solution to the problem. Sometimes it aggravated the problem. But in itself, the self-stimulation was not wrong. At least it enabled the individual to keep up his sexual function while he worked at finding a solution to his social difficulties.

We conclude that any time intercourse is enjoyed less than two or three times a week, it is to be expected that masturbation will be needed to keep the body in "sexual condition." The old adage "use it or lose it" certainly applies here, possibly more than in any other human activity.

What About Just Finding Another Woman?

Some men are so strongly opposed to masturbation that they honestly believe they're better off if they find another woman. Adultery or fornication, in other words, is better than that horrible act of self-stimulation. Such men find partners who will accept them for sex, but with whom they never form emotional relationships. If sex with their wives would become more frequent, they'd never "go outside" again. Incidentally, don't jump to the conclusion that women involved in such "outside" relationships are always victims. There are women who want a purely sexual relationship, too. Some are married, and like the men they "use," they just need more sex. This isn't a behavior pattern that is found only in males.

Bud, another of our clients, is a good example of this type. He talked a great deal about his wife and children and what a great family he had. There was only one problem, he said: His wife just wasn't interested in sex. They had been married for fifteen years, and for the last five years, he had had an "outside" sex partner.

This woman worked in his office. About once a week he'd go to her house, they'd have dinner together, and then they'd have sex. He never spent much time with her, since they had very little in common. "Sally's someone to have sex with once in a while. She doesn't have a steady boyfriend, so it's good for her, too."

We asked if he'd consider divorcing his wife to marry Sally.

"Oh, no. Neither of us want that. If I could get things going with my wife again, I wouldn't see Sally again. She'd understand. I know if she found someone who gave her good sex and who had more interests that matched hers, we wouldn't see each other again, either. But I don't really know what I'd do if that happened. I might not be so lucky with the next woman I found. I know Sally will never do anything to jeopardize my marriage. And if I found another woman who liked the same things I do, that would be bad, too."

We asked why he pursued this relationship when he knew it wasn't going anywhere.

"Because I know I can't hurt Sally. We both just want the sex. I'd feel guilty if I thought I was hurting her."

We asked why he didn't just masturbate. After all, in a way, that was all he was doing with Sally, except that they were using each other to do it.

He looked surprised. "I can't do that. It's not right." Then he smiled. "Funny, isn't it? I'm willing to cheat on my wife with another woman, but I won't masturbate. I feel too guilty for that."

So it is with many men. The guilt runs deep. But there are people who accept masturbation as natural, and who include it as an important part of their sex lives.

One common belief is that only a woman is frustrated when the duration of sex is short. But we have had men come to us because, even though they ejaculate and have orgasm, they still feel unsatisfied. Sometimes, such a man has sex more than once a day, attempting to make up in numbers what he misses in quality. Some scientists believe that there are natural chemicals released into the bloodstream with touch. Other physical changes are known to take place in the body with sexual arousal and response. We speculate that with some people the short duration of sexual activity does not allow these changes to occur. Therefore the sense of well-being that usually accompanies intercourse may not be achieved, leaving the person frustrated and seeking further touching activity, which in our culture usually means sex. We find that often such a man needs only to learn to last longer, so that his body can fully experience the tension and release that comes with satisfying sex. For such a man, multi-orgasms are important.

The same thing is seen in women who are unsatisfied sexually. We find that when these people learn to make sex last longer, the body tensions they feel dissipate. So if you often find yourself feeling oddly unsatisfied, even after a good "quicky," you have an additional reason for cultivating the ability to draw sex out as long as possible.

And when you've done that, you're well on your way to multiple-orgasms.

8

You Can Learn to Multiply Orgasms

Much of the last chapter was taken up with the arguments and the techniques men use to avoid masturbation. Now we must return to the men who use masturbation to get acquainted with their own bodies—the men who came to us claiming they were multi-orgasmic. They used masturbation to get the most from their bodies. They had no need to concern themselves with a partner while they were learning.

That is why we have emphasized the importance of masturbation to you. It's the quickest way for you to learn the lessons we have to teach. After you have learned how to have multiple orgasms alone you can try them with a partner. But if you insist on avoiding masturbation as a tool for learning, you will take longer to master the skill. And maybe you will never learn it at all.

One thing to consider. In the past, you have probably masturbated in a hurry, afraid you'd be caught at it. Now you must take a different approach. We want you to keep it up for a long time. Relax, avoid any pressure that will make you cut short the time you have set aside. Long, drawn-out self-stimulation is the temporary learning device you are going to use in becoming multi-orgasmic. Whether you use it again after that will be up to you.

Remember, masturbation is self-stimulation designed to result in erotic pleasure. It, in itself, is not ever a problem. It can be a help. And in the goal you seek, it is very important.

Actually, for the purposes of your becoming multiorgasmic, we will redefine masturbation and call it a tool—a device you can use to change your sex pattern. We urge the use of masturbation because:

1. You won't have to worry about anyone other than yourself while you're learning.

2. You don't even have to feel particularly "sexy" when you start. In fact, you'll find things work better if you don't try to practice the things we tell you to do when you're "horny." Your need for release will interfere with your awareness of the changes that are occurring in your body.

3. You're looking for ejaculatory control. Like any skill that requires self-awareness, this is difficult to accomplish if you're distracted. When you're alone you have a better chance of reaching your goal.

In therapy, when we're dealing with a man who has problems with erections or wishes to go longer, we tell him to masturbate at least two or three times a week for twenty minutes or more each time.

Even if he isn't interested.

Even if he doesn't feel "sexy" at all.

It's the stimulation of the genitalia that is, in itself, the goal. If, after twenty minutes, the man feels a wish to ejaculate, that's okay. It won't affect the exercise if he does. But many men don't. What they are learning is that it is as important to keep the genitalia in "peak" condition as it is to keep any other part of the body in shape. No one is embarrassed at the thought that they need to exercise their legs, or their lungs. So consider your sex organs as just another part of you that needs to be kept in trim. And just as jogging is good for the legs, so masturbation is good for the sex organs.

There is one thing that needs to be made clear: Multi-orgasmic men typically do not feel ashamed or guilty about masturbation, but at the same time, they aren't addicted to it or dependent on it. They never worry that they will develop such an "addiction." That's the attitude you need to develop.

The best tool to use in learning to be multi-orgasmic and to go longer during sex is masturbation. Not necessarily the way you've done it before, however. Now, your aim is not to "get off" quickly, but to move slowly, using gentle strokes. You want to make this last as long as possible. To start with, lie on your back with your knees bent and slightly apart. We urge that you use this position because multi-orgasmic men seem to prefer the man-on-his-back, woman-on-top position, and you are now trying to develop into a multi-orgasmic man. This position will also allow an easy transition from masturbation to intercourse.

Some positions and methods used during masturbation aren't compatible with intercourse. Chuck's procedure was a good example. Chuck learned to masturbate, as most boys do, when he was about twelve. "I found that if I crossed my ankles and rotated my hips with my penis between my legs, it felt really good. I learned to ejaculate that way. But now I can't ejaculate when I have intercourse."

He said he had had sex with at least fifty women, and never ejaculated with any of them. It frustrated and embarrassed him. He had to "assume his old position" in order to ejaculate.

We asked if he had ever tried to masturbate using his hand.

He said no. "It's wrong to touch yourself there."

Who, we asked him, had told him that?

"No one. But it just isn't right."

We smiled. "Will your penis fall off?"

He laughed aloud. "No."

"You'll go to hell?"

He laughed louder. "No."

"So why is it wrong?"

"I don't know. No reason, I guess. It's silly, but I feel that way. Can you help me?"

We had to convince him first that he should touch his penis, since masturbation was a necessary part of his therapy. Then we offered him some options. He could work in the lab, if he wished, where he would get positive reinforcement as he progressed. We promised to hook him up to our machines to provide additional information as he worked. He agreed to that immediately.

When he came in, we had a therapy team, composed of a male and a female, work with him. They helped him by giving suggestions about how to move his hands, and they also kept an eye on the machines and told him what was happening with his responses.

Another option he was given was to be connected to a "masturbation machine," so he didn't have to touch himself. We advised against that, since he needed to learn to feel more relaxed about his body. This he agreed with, so the machine was set aside.

We told him to lie on his back during his "lessons," for the reasons we've mentioned before, and he agreed. As he followed our instructions, he gradually freed himself from his old masturbatory pattern, and when he left us, he was able to ejaculate during intercourse.

We find in therapy that most men prefer to have the woman on top. We also find that many women don't, at first, like that position. They seem to feel that men should do most of the "work" of sex.

However, if a man is to be multi-orgasmic, he needs strength. When he is in the superior position, he is under great physical strain. He must hold himself up so as not to crush his partner. After he has one orgasm in this position, he's usually totally exhausted. He falls back on the bed and goes to sleep. And no wonder—he's been exercising very strenuously.

It's different when he's on his back: He can relax more. The woman on top does not have to work as hard as he did; she's usually lighter, so she isn't in danger of crushing him. She has an additional benefit. Since she's more in control of the movements, she can adjust the action to fit her needs. Generally, when we explain this, couples agree to try the woman-superior position, and find that they prefer it, after all.

Lesson Time

Most men masturbate by grabbing the penis and moving the hand up and down the shaft. That's how we want you to do it. But you've probably moved your hand quickly in the past. You should change now. We want you to move your hand slowly, gently, using a light touch. You are to try to use about the same pressure as you'd feel from the walls of the vagina during intercourse. We find that some cases of ejaculatory "incompetence" are caused because a man is accustomed to masturbating with a firm pressure of his fingers—a pressure far greater than he experiences when he has intercourse. When a man comes to therapy complaining of this problem, the first thing we ask him is how he holds his penis when he masturbates. Often, when he adjusts this pressure to match the pressure of a vagina, his problem is solved.

Ken had been through other sex therapy before he came to us. He was surprised at our question. "I've been asked before if I ejaculated when I masturbated, but no one has ever asked me about the pressure I used. I never thought it made any difference. I just thought that being with a woman would turn me on so everything would be okay."

It took Ken a few weeks to adjust to this change in his masturbation pattern. Because it was important to him, he worked conscientiously to make the adjustment. When he ended his therapy, he was ejaculating with intercourse. Nine months later, we received a birth announcement from Ken and his very happy wife. Our therapy had been successful.

Squeeze Play

If you've read other books about sex, you have probably heard of the *squeeze technique*. We use it extensively in our therapy, for it provides a man with a method for extending the time during sex before he ejaculates. If you're able to go for fifteen to twenty minutes without ejaculating during masturbation or intercourse, you probably don't need to practice this exercise, but we suggest that you do it anyway, so that you master the technique. You will then be equipped to handle unexpected changes in your sexual lifestyle.

What kind of changes? The most obvious is having something happen to limit your sexual activity temporarily, or cut it off entirely. When, after a period of deprivation, men resume sexual activity, they tend to ejaculate far too quickly, at least for a time. If you know how to use the squeeze technique, you can get things under control much faster.

Three different techniques can be used to delay ejaculation during masturbation and intercourse. Right now, they apply only to masturbation. The first (1) is the squeeze technique. The second (2) is tightening the PC muscle. The third (3) is to keep your testicles from moving up close to your body (more on this later).

The squeeze technique (1) is done by placing the first two fingers on the underside of the penis and the thumb on top. In this position, squeeze tightly. The picture (below) will illustrate what we mean.

Squeeze Technique

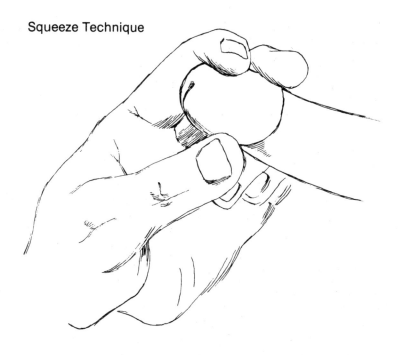

When this is done, the penis may grow larger, it may go completely limp, or it may remain somewhere in between as far as firmness is concerned. Whatever happens, don't worry. Just hold the tight pressure for fifteen seconds, and then begin the back-and-forth movement again, whether you still have an erection or not, for at least twenty minutes. Use the squeeze as often as you have to to stop yourself from ejaculating. As your confidence increases, you'll find that you don't have to use "the squeeze" as often. Sometimes, you can let your PC muscles (2) take over, tightening them instead of squeezing. Sometimes you'll do best if you use both techniques. But don't set any limits for yourself. Men who have sex daily are more apt to reach the point of ejaculatory control quicker than men who don't have sex often. Some men reach this control within a week—others have taken up to six months. The important thing is to keep up the practice. Perseverance pays off, in this as in any other form of physical training.

Once you can go for fifteen or twenty minutes without having to squeeze, it is time for you to move to the next step. Now you'll work to get as close to what is called "ejaculatory inevitability" as you can before you squeeze. You'll feel it approaching if you're attentive to your body changes. Most men, we find, are able to tell us when they're going to have an orgasm.

You'll want to use this squeeze technique as close to that point as possible. The object is to stop yourself from ejaculating but not from having an orgasm. At first you probably won't have much luck. You'll miss that critical point, maybe only by microseconds. But the day will come when you'll be right on the dot.

When this happens, you'll find that you can repeat the process, each time with greater ease. There will still be misses, but there will be more successes each time you masturbate. In time you'll be able to hold off on your ejaculation until you're ready to end your sex session. You'll find, incidentally, that the intensity of each orgasm will be greater and remain high for a longer time when you do not ejaculate.

Ejaculatory Inevitability

A bit more about ejaculatory inevitability. It's important that you learn to recognize this moment. Pay attention to your feelings and to the changes that take place in your body. You may feel the sensation without even having an erection. Don't let that surprise you. An erection isn't necessary for orgasm—or for the use of the squeeze technique.

If you have trouble locating that moment of "no-return," use this plan. As soon as you get an erection (even a "small" one), use the squeeze technique, holding for fifteen seconds. Then return to the up-and-down movement that stimulates you, remembering to keep it gentle and light. Do a few strokes, and squeeze again. Next time, let a little more time pass before you squeeze. If you don't feel any need to ejaculate, extend the time more. You'll locate that point of no return for your body in that manner. A few miscues along the way are to be expected. Don't let them worry you. After all, you're learning something new. Don't expect a perfect record with no errors on the way.

We've found that for most men there is a period after the point of ejaculatory inevitability and before ejaculation when there is intense pleasure. It lasts for about five seconds, and then the semen is expelled. You want to come as close to that point as possible, so you don't interrupt the pleasure sequence, but rather extend it. This will occur by stopping ejaculation. If you find that moment, you'll cut off the flow, but not the sensations. From what our subjects tell us, you'll experience pure ecstasy.

Keep Them Down

All this will be easier if you have followed our advice and are masturbating slowly. Slow movements allow you to identify every change that takes place in your body.

One change that will be quite obvious will come about in your testicles. Normally, they hang in the scrotal sac, several inches below the base of the penis. You can lift them with your pelvic muscles or with your hand. During sexual arousal, the scrotal sac tightens and lifts the testicles up against the body. You can't ejaculate unless they're in that position. So, to postpone ejaculation, you can pull the scrotum down manually, keeping the testicles down far enough to keep them from assuming the position that will make ejaculation inevitable (3). Some men do this by holding their testicles between their legs as they masturbate, and sometimes even while they have intercourse.

Lesson Time—Again!

You don't think you need a lesson in how to masturbate?
Think again.

Most men learned to masturbate when they were boys,
and they were always afraid they'd be caught. So how did
they do it?

Right! As quickly as they could. They kept their bodies
tense, and they moved their hands very quickly. What's
more, they grasped the penis far too firmly.

If you learned that method, give this new one a try. This
is the technique that will pave the way to your becoming
multi-orgasmic. And that's your goal, isn't it?

So we're going to spell it all out—even though we'll be
repeating much that you already know, or have read on the
preceding pages of this book.

1. Get comfortable and relaxed. Lie down on your back,
preferably on a bed.

2. Have your knees bent and slightly apart.

3. Gently, lightly, stroke your inner thighs and up your
body all the way to your nipples. Be sure to spend time
caressing your penis and scrotum.

4. Take the penis at the base with your thumb and
index finger and move the foreskin gently and slowly toward the end of the penis and back. If you're circumcised,
your strokes should be a bit shorter, or your fingers should
slide a bit more. Be gentle. And keep it slow.

5. Stroke your nipples (yes, men have nerve endings in
their nipples, just as women do) with the hand that isn't
stroking your penis. The nipples will grow hard (erect). Even
if you don't think you have any response there, do it. Your
body will react.

6. Stroke your penis gently from base to head with
slow, light strokes.

7. Use pressure on the penis that is about as much as

you'll get from the walls of the vagina. If you don't know what that would be, then use the force of a light-to-medium handshake. Avoid any hard, over-firm pressure. You'll be training yourself to ejaculate during sexual intercourse, and most vaginas aren't that tight.

8. Continue the up-and-down stroking for twenty minutes. See how much pleasure you can get without speeding up and working toward ejaculation. If you can, keep your testicles down. When you feel yourself getting close to orgasm, use the squeeze technique, or tighten your PC muscles.

9. Use the squeeze technique whenever you get close to ejaculation. Squeeze for fifteen or twenty seconds, release, and go back to stroking. Don't worry if your penis loses some degree of erection.

10. Let your mind wander to the most pleasurable sexual things you can think of. If it adds to your enjoyment, read an erotic book or look at erotic pictures in a magazine.

11. After you are able to masturbate for fifteen to twenty minutes without ejaculating (with the use of the squeeze technique), see how close to ejaculatory inevitability you can come and still not ejaculate. Use the squeeze technique when necessary, and also tighten the pelvic muscle and use the technique of holding your testicles away from your body.

12. See if you can have an orgasm without ejaculating. You may find a little semen coming out. Don't worry. Many men who are multi-orgasmic ejaculate a little semen with each orgasm.

13. Masturbate at least two or three times a week.

14. Take time to pleasure yourself. Find a time when you won't be interrupted. If necessary, lock your bedroom door. Remember, the name of the game is fun. Do what you feel like doing. If you like to use a vibrator, use it. If you prefer to fondle silk or feathers while you masturbate, go ahead. Everything goes when you're by yourself, as long as

it's not hurtful. Do what you need to do to gain the utmost pleasure. Expect pleasure. If you can masturbate for at least twenty to thirty minutes with uninterrupted pleasure, it will make no difference to you whether you have one orgasm during the time or a dozen.

15. Remember that you want to establish a pattern that will be easily transferred to intercourse. It doesn't have to be done in the position we've described, even though we've found it works best for most men. You're an individual. You have to accept your own way—and your own body. Do what's right for you.

9

Don't Be Afraid to Masturbate

We've said a lot already about masturbation. Maybe, for some of you, we seem to be making far too much of it. But we have a reason. In our experience, both with clients and at lectures, we have encountered very strong resistance to the act—and even to any discussion of it. We are aware that it is popularly assumed that everyone in our modern society is comfortable with nudity and sex, that only a few people still remain who fear masturbation. But popular belief and reality do not seem to coincide in this area.

We have found that a very small number of Americans are totally at ease with masturbation. If you are one of those, just skip this chapter.

But if, in spite of everything we've said, you still don't want to masturbate, then read on. For all that we've said, masturbation still isn't the only road to your becoming multi-orgasmic. But being willing to masturbate is. It's the attitude that's important. From 1968 through 1982, we've seen approximately five thousand research subjects and clients. They've given us many reasons why they couldn't (or wouldn't) masturbate. Maybe you have one that's unique. But more probably, you have used one of the excuses we'll list now.

1. My value system forbids it.
2. I don't know how.
3. Masturbation is for kids—not men.
4. I'm afraid I'll get hooked, and stop enjoying intercourse.
5. I don't need to. I have all the sex I need—the right way.
6. If I get to enjoy masturbation, maybe I won't be able to function with a partner anymore.
7. My religion forbids it.
8. It's evil—of the devil.
9. It's too much work.
10. I don't have the time.
11. My partner wouldn't want me to masturbate.
12. What would my friends think—if they knew I was doing it?

If you just can't overcome your objection to masturbation, don't despair. There are other methods that can be explored. They won't be as easy, but they will work. If you're willing to stick to it, we'll show you what to do.

But before we abandon the easiest way to practice, let's give it another try. Here are our answers to those objections.

To start with, we'll bypass the ones that deal with religion and value systems. We'll get back to them later.

2. You don't know how. Well, we're here to teach you how, so that objection is no good. If you read this book carefully, you'll have more information about masturbation than you thought existed.

3. Kid stuff? Not at all. Masturbation is used by adults from twenty to ninety. It fills a definite need. There's nothing childish about giving yourself pleasure. As the ads say, "You deserve it."

4. You think you might get hooked. In all of our studies, we have never encountered a sane, undisturbed person who was "hooked" on masturbation. But were that to happen to

a man, he could seek help in eliminating that addiction, just as you can get help in "unhooking" yourself from drug addiction, or an addiction to cigarettes.

5. You don't need to. You have enough sex—of the right kind. There's nothing "wrong" about masturbation. It is as "right" as intercourse. Each has its place. And what if a time comes when you don't have enough intercourse? Why wait until then to learn the technique?

6. Maybe you won't be able to function in intercourse anymore. No danger! Some of our best subjects—men who are masters at pleasing a female partner and themselves— tell us that they masturbate regularly. Both practices can exist side-by-side.

9 and 10. Too much work; not enough time. If you like tennis, do you avoid it because it's too much work, or because it takes too much time out of your life? Of course not. Well, you'll find the pleasure you receive from effective masturbation more than overshadows the effort and time involved.

11. My partner wouldn't like me to do it. Have you asked her? Have you both read what we say about the benefits of this practice? If she still says no, then you will have to take another path to multi-orgasms. But if she knows you bought this book, and approves of the purchase, she isn't apt to object to your practicing the easiest way.

12. What would my friends think? If you discuss your sexual activities with your friends, they'll probably be in awe, especially if you tell them that you had learned to become multi-orgasmic by masturbating. They'd probably go right out and buy their own copy of this book.

1, 7, and 8. We have no wish to disturb anyone's religious beliefs. However, be sure you aren't just hanging on to some childhood prohibition and using a religious justification for your attitude. If you really have religious objections to masturbation, then you'll have to go some other route.

A few more words about the possibility of anyone becoming "addicted" to masturbation. There are volumes of evidence that "excessive" masturbation (which actually interferes with a man's normal living) is related to pressing emotional problems. If you are a normal man with a normal range of interests, you have little chance of developing an addiction to sex—but you certainly can learn to appreciate and enjoy it more.

Are There Alternatives?

If you have strong religious inhibitions against masturbation, there are other ways to reach your goal of becoming multi-orgasmic. You can continue to strengthen your PC muscle, and tighten it instead of using the squeeze technique to stop ejaculation. It won't be as easy—but it can be done.

As for a substitute for masturbation, try this: When you are having intercourse, have your partner continue thrusting after she has an orgasm. If you feel that you're about to ejaculate, and you don't want to, have her tighten her PC muscle as you tighten yours. (You can see that she'll have to do the same exercises you do to strengthen that very important muscle.)

Even if you do ejaculate, have her keep up the movement. There's no reason why you have to stop intercourse when you ejaculate. That's just one more pattern we've accepted without question. Momentary penile sensitivity after orgasm is usually dissipated in a few seconds. This brief period should not interfere with continuing movement. Brief pauses in ongoing coitus frequently occur.

The Masturbation Machine

A modern invention is helpful here. It's called a self-stimulator by some manufacturers. We use it when we have a handicapped or elderly client who would find even slow manual masturbation too exhausting. Such clients usually tire more easily than do healthy or younger men, and fatigue is often the cause of early ejaculation. If a man is too quickly exhausted, he may even abandon intercourse or masturbation entirely, and not have an orgasm (or ejaculate) at all.

Cliff, a client, has been handicapped for fifteen years. He'd been told by his doctor that he would never have erections again—nor would he ejaculate.

"They told me I was terminal, too," he said, smugly, "but I've outlived both of them." (He was referring to his doctors.) When he came to us he expressed a wish to see if "they" had been wrong about his sex life, too.

We put him on the masturbation machine, and he not only had an erection, he ejaculated. We continued to use the machine throughout his therapy, and by the time he was finished, he had recovered his ability to have sex without using any outside aid.

He was understandably pleased. "I guess I didn't really think I'd be able to do it," he said on his last visit. "I still need help, of course. Someone has to put me in position, and my partner has to do all the moving. But with her help, I can get my penis in, and we can have good sex. I feel wonderful about it. Everything in my life has more meaning now. I'm more motivated to do things I thought I'd never enjoy again. I'm even back in physical therapy. Life has meaning for me again."

If you're handicapped, you might want to buy one of these machines. You'll find the name of a manufacturer in the Appendix, on page 168.

There are several kinds of stimulator machines, but the one we find most useful is a small portable model. It has a handle on the case, and various sizes of sleeves that fit around the penis. The sleeves and other parts of the machine can easily fit into a small paper bag if you want to carry it somewhere. Our clients usually choose one or two sleeves that they want to try to use. A condom is slipped onto the penis before it is put into one of the sleeves, and either Vaseline or a special lubricant sold by the manufacturer is applied to prevent irritation. Our clients who have taken the machines home report that it is very portable.

The action of this machine is much like the action of a milking machine. Our clients use it in either of two ways:

1. The sleeve can be made to move up and down the shaft of the penis.
2. The machine can be held at the base of the penis, where it produces a slight squeezing effect.

There are warnings. Don't set the machine at too high a speed. If you do, it may produce ejaculation without orgasm, actually "milking" your glans. While this won't harm you, it is certainly not what you're working for. You want to be able to have orgasms *without ejaculation*—not the opposite.

If you buy one of these machines, set it at its slowest speed. Let your erection and your responses build slowly. You'll still have to touch your penis when you apply the squeeze technique—or your partner will have to do it. At that point, it might be easier if you pull the sleeve off, so it doesn't interfere with your squeezing. Tightening the PC muscle can help hold back ejaculation, too, if it's done at the same time as you squeeze.

If you want to keep the machine going even while you're tightening your PC muscle, you definitely must set it at its slowest speed. The idea is the same as if you were using your hand. You want orgasm to occur, but not ejaculation.

Despite their objections to manual masturbation, some

people are "turned off" by the machines, which they find "too mechanical." Once again, we're up against an unreasonable reaction. Such people often have visions of sex as being some sort of magical, mystical experience, even though they have never themselves found it to be that way. They feel a machine destroys the magic. When we come up against such opposition, we have to undo years of conditioning before we can proceed with the lessons.

Incidentally, we have mentioned that the squeeze technique can be used by men who have hypospadia or epispadia, when the urethral opening is either on the underside or the top of the penis, instead of toward the tip. When such a condition exists, you can squeeze anywhere on the penis, below the urethral opening toward the base.

We mention this here, because if you are using the machine and wish to leave it on, just before you reach ejaculatory inevitability, you can squeeze at the base to avoid ejaculation.

Remember the advice given before. Persevere. Don't give up if you fail the first few times you try. People who succeed at the tasks they set for themselves do so because they keep on trying until they win.

As for the machine, once you've mastered the art of having multiple orgasms, you can put it aside. It's served its purpose.

What Do You Call Masturbation?

Joan, a minister's wife and a very proper lady, was shocked when we asked her if she masturbated. "I never masturbate." We could tell she hated to use the word. "Never have. It's against my religious principles."

We duly noted her response and continued with her sexual history.

Some questions later we asked how she achieved orgasm, since she had already informed us that she did not orgasm during sex with her husband. We had difficulty containing our reaction when she answered.

"Well," she spoke softly. "I use my vibrator a couple of times a week. I usually orgasm two or three times with that. I just can't have an orgasm any other way."

It was easy to understand that to her the word masturbation had a limited definition. It meant only "touching the genitalia with the hands." And her attitude was clear. She would never do that, because that was "sinful."

Before you male readers have a good laugh, consider that the same response has been given by men as well. A young client, a Muslim student from the Middle East, was anxious because his wife was coming to visit him. The last two times he had gone home to see her he had not been able to have an erection, and this worried him.

He explained to us that because of his religious beliefs, he could not have extramarital sex, and that meant that when he wanted another woman, he divorced his present wife and married a new one. This current wife, who was coming to visit him, was his fourth. He assured us that he had never had sex outside of marriage, nor had he ever masturbated.

He repeated his opposition to masturbation when we suggested that masturbation might serve as a method for keeping his sexual organs in working condition during the long periods of deprivation when his wife was not close by. Again he responded by assuring us that he could not— would not—masturbate. "Is there not some other way?" he asked.

He was delighted when we showed him the masturbation machine. If he used that, he told us, he would not have to "pollute himself" by touching his penis. In his culture, the hand that holds the penis when a man urinates (always the left hand) is considered unclean, and is never used to touch food or the hand of a friend.

He took the machine home with him, and on the next visit reported success. "This is going to do it," he announced with obvious happiness. "I am now getting erections. I thank you so very much."

Several months later, we received a phone call from him in which he reported that everything was now going well for him. His erections were still firm. We suggested that he might buy his own machine, since this had been what resolved his problem, and he agreed. He realized that the pelvic exercises he was doing were not quite enough to keep him in good sexual condition.

Another young man, a devotee of yoga, also expressed a fear of "pollution" during masturbation. However, his main worry was with the semen he ejaculated, since he masturbated twice a week. His problem was not solved by the masturbation machine, since it did not in itself control the flow of semen when he ejaculated.

For this young man, who worried very much about "excessive masturbation," nothing would help until he mastered the technique of holding back ejaculation while permitting orgasm. Yet his fear of weakening himself because of the "constant ejection of his life force during masturbation" handicapped him in the learning process.

It did us no good to reassure him that masturbation was normal, nor did he accept our statement that ejaculation would not weaken him. For him, the entire process of learning sexual control was too fraught with psychic danger.

Under circumstances like this, the important need is for the individual to hold to his own value system. What good would it have done this young man to learn to be multiorgasmic, or even to gain greater control of his sexual processes, if he could no longer face himself?

You, too, must squarely confront your own value system and be certain that what we ask you to do does not violate some deeply entrenched concept that you use as a guide in your life.

Overcoming Objections

Tony was convinced that he could never masturbate, even though we had carefully explained that masturbation could serve as the path by which he might be able to have erections. For him, the problem was long-standing. He had been born with a congenital defect in his penis. From the age of six on, he had a series of operations designed to correct that defect.

Several years before he came to us, he had had one final operation, after which he was informed that he would never have an erection. He sought us out because he was beginning to think that the doctor had been wrong. "I feel sensations in my penis. It isn't unresponsive—not entirely, anyway. Sometimes it feels fuller than it does at other times, although I haven't really had an erection. Still, I can't help but want to try."

However, he was convinced that masturbation was not for him. We asked if he had religious objections to the act.

He said no. "But my mother was against it. She said I'd have real trouble if I did it. I know it's silly. But she really hammered the idea in my head. I'm just sure I'd have more problems if I began to masturbate. But it isn't because I'm religious. Hell, I'm an agnostic. But I know that if I begin to masturbate, I'll hear my mother telling me that I'm a bad boy. I know it's foolish. And I'll do it if you insist. But if there's any other way, it would cause me a lot less problems."

We all joined in a laugh. It was clear where he was coming from. Even if he agreed to masturbate because we insisted, he'd be so tense that there would be little chance that he'd make any gains in learning the control he wanted.

We suggested a surrogate, and again he laughed. He smiled as he replied.

"You don't have sex until you're married—and on top of that, you have to love her."

When we suggested the "self-stimulation machine," he brightened. We explained that the machine would work if he could relax and let it. We also told him that it might produce an erection. Whatever happened, if he used the machine for a while, he would have a better idea of his potential. "Of course," we added, "you could have a prothesis inserted, or get a penile implant that you can pump up when you want an erection."

"No." He spoke firmly. "No more operations. I'd rather be impotent."

He had his first session with the machine in the laboratory. We suggested that he have the usual male/female team working with him to serve as guides, but he rejected that idea. He preferred to do it alone, with a consultation with us afterward, and with the understanding that if he had a problem, we would be nearby to help him.

He did not, however, need help. When he finished his session, he came in to talk. No, he had not had a full erection. "But I did feel a lot. There's definitely something there the doctor didn't recognize."

We asked him to rate his erection on a scale from 1 to 10, but he hesitated. "I can't do that very well. I've never experienced a ten." However, he finally said he thought it was about a three, and announced that he definitely wanted to try it again.

He came in for several more sessions at the lab, and each time the results were slightly more than before. At last we suggested that he take the portable machine home and continue on his own. We made an appointment with him for six weeks later.

He was smiling delightedly when he came in. "I'm having erections that are at least a seven on the scale," he announced triumphantly. Pleased, we sent him home again with the machine, after setting up another appointment.

Six weeks later he returned with even better news. He was now having an occasional full erection.

Once more he returned home with the machine, to return in six more weeks.

This time he surprised us both. "I can stimulate myself to erection now." He was obviously pleased. "And I don't always use the machine. I realized that I couldn't use the machine if I was going to have a partner. She'd think I was crazy. So I decided that Mother had to go." He laughed.

We asked how he felt about what had taken place, and he laughed again. "Fine. You know, when you didn't try to push me into doing anything, I got to thinking. You made it clear how important it was for me to dare to masturbate, but you still told me to stay with my feelings. But in these last weeks I've come to realize that I don't feel the same as I used to. I tried touching myself, and I didn't feel guilty at all. So I decided that it was more important for me to get free from the machine than it was for me to obey something my mother had said when I was a child."

He smiled again, evidently remembering what he had experienced. "You know, it's a lot harder for me to get an erection without that machine. But I'm working on it. I'd like to be like a normal man—and normal men don't walk around with their own private little erection machines when they go on dates."

We suggested that there would be many girls who wouldn't object to the machine, if he explained what it was and why he needed it. He agreed. If he found that he had to work too long without the machine before he could get an erection, he'd continue to use it. But he still wanted as much freedom from it as he could have.

He explained that already he was able to keep an erection up after the machine had brought him up, if he just kept on stroking himself. "I figure that I can't expect a girl to spend an hour just to bring me to erection. But if she'll be willing to stimulate me after I get it up, I know I can maintain it, and we can have intercourse."

Tony later bought his own machine, and reported to us

that he was able to use it as he had said he would, to start things going.

We have not used the masturbation machine in our laboratory for the specific purpose of training men to be multi-orgasmic. But we find that as an alternative to "manual" masturbation it is very valuable and effective. For that reason, we decided that there was no reason why it could not be effective as a tool in developing multi-orgasms in men who used it properly. Certainly the machine would eliminate the impediment that holds many men back from doing the exercises that must be done to achieve multi-orgasms.

We were pleased and not surprised when two men who own Accu Jac machines reported that they have become multi-orgasmic since they began using the devices. Admittedly, this is mere anecdotal information, not acceptable as scientific data, but it is encouraging, nevertheless. We are not generally asked to teach men to be multi-orgasmic. When a client develops that skill, it is a by-product of other remedial work. However, we have suggested that some clients might wish to work for that goal as they also worked to remedy the problems that brought them to us. We consider that as a possible bonus to their "cure," one that seems to give both the men involved and their partners much pleasure.

10

All Together Now!

We've seen women who truly wanted to help their partners become more effective sexually—women who care that much. If you're one of the lucky men who has a partner who is chafing at the bit, wondering when—and if—she'll be able to help you to your goal of being multi-orgasmic, don't keep her out of your exercises.

A willing, loving partner can be very helpful, as we have shown in some of the past case histories. A woman can perform the squeeze technique as effectively as can a man, if he is comfortable having her do it, and if she wants to.

For some men, this cooperative method of working is another alternative that is most attractive. These men, who are usually strongly opposed to masturbation, do not object to this form of manual manipulation. They feel that it's more akin to "normal" sexual behavior, since the touching is being done by another. We certainly approve, especially if this technique works for them.

However, in order to clarify things, let us repeat something we've said before. The PC exercises and the masturbation exercises can both be done without a partner. It's important that a single man understand this. In fact, we suggest that the exercises specifically designed for the male be done when he's alone, even if he *has* a loving partner, as long as he's comfortable with masturbation. These exercises seem to be mastered far quicker when he can concentrate on them.

What we're going to talk about now are nondemand exercises that were first introduced by Masters and Johnson. These are specifically designed to encourage a man and woman to feel comfortable together, and to encourage relaxation. Specific nondemand exercises are described and depicted in Masters and Johnson, *Human Sexual Inadequacy,* and in Hartman and Fithian, *Treatment of Sexual Dysfunction.* The former is available in most bookstores and the latter can be ordered from the address given on page 168.

The Body Caress

Relaxation is the key to any kind of learning. It is even more important when your goal is to become multi-orgasmic. The exercises we will speak of next are very relaxing for both of you. You will touch each others' bodies with eyes closed, sending warm messages of love through touch alone. No talking should be done. Talking is mental; you are to communicate with your bodies, not your voices.

We suggest the following procedure:

1. Start with a "warm-up." Using your fingers, and touching very lightly, stroke your partner's body all over. Change roles every once in a while, so neither of you tires.
2. Start with the back of the body, making certain that you touch every inch of skin before your partner turns over.
3. When you caress the front of the body, don't concentrate on the genitals. Right now, you just want to share the pleasure of being touched and of touching.
4. Keep this up for at least two hours. This way each partner will have, at a minimum, a full hour of being caressed. If that seems like a long time, consider this: How long has it been since you received that much pleasure from

anyone? Maybe you never have before. We all like to be petted. We want to be certain that you continue this step until you both feel very, very loved.

After two hours of caressing, you will both be ready for the next step.

Nondemand Pleasuring

Now one of you will provide what we call "nondemand pleasuring" for from ten to fifteen minutes. At the end of that time, switch roles. If you both enjoyed what happened, repeat the process. If you want, repeat it again. Do the entire sequence of caressing and pleasuring two or three times a week. Use it as foreplay—or let it be something you do just for the pleasure it gives you both. Whatever you decide, don't let yourself get into a rut. *Body caressing or nondemand pleasuring should not be locked in as foreplay.* If it is, one or the other of you may find it too demanding, and hesitate to continue with it.

Basically, what we're saying is that you should be very clear about your objectives each time you start this activity. Is your goal to become multi-orgasmic? Then say that at the outset. Are you just looking for a good "opening" for sex? Put your cards on the table, and give your partner an opportunity to say no. Don't start what is supposed to be body caress or nondemand pleasuring and then accuse your partner of being a "prick teaser" if she wants to stop without having intercourse. That isn't fair.

The best position for you and your partner to be in when you are being pleasured is as follows:

1. She should sit on the bed with her back against the headboard. She can use a pillow behind her for extra comfort. Her legs should be separated, as far apart as is comfortable.

2. You lie on your back with your legs over hers at the thigh area, with your pelvis in what would be her lap were her legs together.

3. Close your eyes and relax.

4. Your partner should stroke your inner thighs and up over your scrotum, testicles, and penis, clear up to your navel.

5. After caressing your abdomen gently, she should move back to your knees and repeat the stroking.

6. If you feel yourself getting close to ejaculation, have your partner do the squeeze. (Remember, this is usually done with the thumb and the two fingers opposite each other, near the base of the head of your penis. She should squeeze as tightly as possible without hurting you.) This will reverse the urge to ejaculate. While she is doing this, you can also tighten your pelvic muscles. This will train you to stop the ejaculation by yourself.

7. After fifteen or twenty seconds of squeezing, your partner can resume the caressing, continuing it until you once more feel the need to ejaculate.

8. The object is for you to go for fifteen to twenty minutes with a good erection (50 percent or more) without needing to squeeze and without ejaculating. It may take a number of practice periods before you reach this point.

9. Once you have gone for the required period without feeling the need to ejaculate, then try to get closer to orgasm than you have before (when you first used the squeeze technique), just as we described in Chapter Eight. Your goal is to be able to let yourself have the orgasm without permitting the ejaculation.

10. Keep working on getting closer and closer to the point of "ejaculatory inevitability" until you actually "slip over" while holding back ejaculation with the squeeze and have a "dry orgasm."

11. Don't give up. Be sure that you show your partner

how much you appreciate what she's doing. There's no doubt that she'll benefit when you reach your goal, but remember, she might be involved at this point only because you won't (or can't) touch yourself.

Nondemand Pleasuring

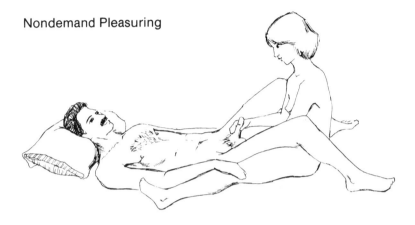

Working Together

When a man masturbates and uses the squeeze technique, he can tell more exactly when to squeeze. After all, he's the one feeling the body changes. When you ask your partner to do the squeezing, you have to let her know in time that you are approaching that important moment.

Her fingers will be just the opposite of yours when you do it. Her thumb will be on the frenum (underside of penis below head) and her first two fingers on either side of the coronal ridge. Or in the case of hypospadias, she can use the thumb and fingers in the same way just below the urethral opening toward the bottom of the shaft.

Now we all know that it's hard to communicate in the best of situations, so we'd better get a few things clear.

1. Many men think they know when ejaculatory inevitability takes place, but they really don't. If you feel your partner has bad timing, consider that you might not be giving her the right cues. Be patient. You're both going to be trying to do your best. Whatever you do, don't let yourself get angry if she misses the moment and you ejaculate.

2. If this happens, take a breather and start again. But try a different technique. You'll recognize it from an earlier chapter. As soon as you are erect again, she should squeeze, holding it for the required fifteen to twenty seconds. Then she should resume the stroking. She should keep this up, gradually extending the time between squeezes, until you are going for fifteen minutes without ejaculating. (This may mean that she has "squeezed" a number of times, and has stopped you from ejaculating more than once.)

3. Now try to go longer between the squeezes. You're trying to get to where both you and your partner can recognize the changes that take place as you approach ejaculatory inevitability. When you reach that goal, you'll be close to the time when you can hold in the ejaculate by squeezing (either you, with your pelvic muscles, or your partner, with her fingers), and still have the experience of an orgasm.

4. When you're through exercising for the day (or afternoon or evening) you may, if you both wish, have intercourse. Or you can just let your erection subside. We suggest that you vary the way you end things, so there never comes a time when the exercise is tied to what follows it.

5. Remember: An erection is desirable for this exercise, but it isn't essential. Two of the men in our multi-orgasmic research were impotent.

6. Eventually, you want to be able to go for the entire fifteen-to-twenty-minute period without having to squeeze at all. That may take some time. However, it is important. Multiple orgasms take time to develop. Be patient with yourself, as well as with your partner.

Once you learn to be multi-orgasmic, you may find that your orgasms start soon after stimulation begins. That's okay; they'll continue for longer periods, and you'll have more than one.

A few more bits of advice:

1. Don't try to work on everything at once. Begin by strengthening your PC muscles. When they're in good condition, then start learning how to stop ejaculation. Don't worry if you fail many times—and don't expect to immediately slide into having "dry" orgasms.

2. Remember that sex should be fun, even when you're learning a new skill. Take things lightly. Don't let yourself feel frustrated if you seem to be getting nowhere for a while. Set one goal, and don't move to the next until you have reached it.

3. When you can stop ejaculating almost every time, then you can move on to the next step. Set goals, but don't ever set a time limit for yourself. If you take one week or one year, it doesn't matter. You'll give up too soon if you forget to have fun along the way.

Consider the possibility that you may not be willing to exert yourself enough to ever become multi-orgasmic. We never said the path was easy. But if you try some of these exercises, both alone and with your partner, you will add variety to your sex lives. And that will be good, too. One wonderful thing about sex: There is no one "right" way to enjoy it.

Getting—and Keeping—It Up

If you've had problems getting erections, your first goal, understandably, will be to develop one. Maybe you know what your problem has been. If it's physiological, then it's probable that no amount of exercising will help. Just remember that this need not stop you from learning to be multi-orgasmic.

Whatever the cause of impotence, it never hurts to try to get an erection, as long as you keep things in perspective. Just do the stimulation exercises regularly, two or three times a week for three weeks. If you are ever going to get an erection, there should be some signs of it by then. You might not have more than a 2 or 3 on a scale of 10, but if you have any response it means that the capability is there.

Usually six weeks of pleasuring such as we described in the beginning of this chapter combined with at least fifty pelvic exercises a day will produce some kind of erection in a man if he's going to get one at all. He'll usually begin by experiencing some genital sensations that, as the weeks progress, will increase until he can get at least a 50 percent erection during pleasuring. That's enough for penetration. In fact, you can insert your penis into a vagina without any erection at all.

If you've never had problems getting an erection, then you can start by trying to slow down your "ejaculatory response." In our work with over a thousand cases, we've found that if a man can learn to go for fifteen to twenty minutes during masturbation or pleasuring, he can go as long as he wants to during intercourse. That period (fifteen to twenty minutes) seems to be critical. Once you've passed it, you have control. It's that simple.

Only, of course, it isn't really simple at all. It sounds far easier than it is. You'll have to practice, exert effort, and be patient. Just remember that many others have succeeded through diligent practice. And it does take practice. In modern terminology, this requires a "hands-on" repetition. It won't be enough if you mentally understand what is supposed to happen. You must experience it yourself.

You must also believe that you can do it. You need to establish a mind set that recognizes your need for control and that doesn't question whether you will—or can—achieve your goal. Put doubts behind you. The more positive your mind set, the more sure your success.

Whether you have an easy or difficult time achieving an erection, you will probably agree that keeping it is another matter. Often, the only problem is one of mind and sensate focus. Most men have worries that often beset them when they have an erection: "Will I keep it long enough?" "Is it big enough?" "Will I function to her satisfaction?"

There are many questions that can interrupt a man's concentration of sexual pleasure. Every one serves to detract from the feelings of arousal that are necessary for an erection to remain hard. If you want to strengthen your erections, learn to concentrate your attention on the pleasure of sex. Learn to be selfish, to take pleasure for yourself as well as to give it. If you don't, you may find that you have little to give. After all, if your mind is wandering off, you can hardly please a partner.

Get involved in the sex you are having. Take pleasure in what is happening to you. This is the best reason for diligent exercise in the various techniques for extending your erection. If you have done the squeeze technique, or held your testicles down, or tightened your pelvic muscles so often that the actions are second nature to you, you'll be able to pay attention to the fun you're having, not to what you should be doing next.

And be prepared for a surprise. Most of our clients who have experienced orgasm without ejaculation have done so as a "bonus" during nondemand pleasuring. You have one advantage over most of them. You know that orgasm can take place without ejaculation. So you can watch for the signs, and be ready to appreciate it when it happens.

A Few Reminders

Sometimes a retrograde ejaculation (when the semen goes into the bladder and is expelled when you urinate) occurs when you use the squeeze technique. It happens to some men, but not to everyone. It may happen to you during nondemand pleasuring. Like any ejaculation, it results in a temporary loss of erection. Don't be concerned; continue the pleasuring anyway.

Another thing that may be of concern to some men looks bad, and may frighten you if it happens to you. To explain it, we must back up a bit.

It isn't uncommon, during intercourse, for a small capillary to break in the penis, sometimes just as ejaculation occurs. Of course, during intercourse the penis is inside the vagina, so no one notices, since there isn't much blood. But when you're pleasuring yourself with a partner you may ejaculate "in the open," so to speak, and then that tiny bit of blood could be frightening. If it happens once, and then never again, you have no need to worry. But if there is blood in your ejaculate on a regular basis, then you should see a doctor.

Even then, don't jump to conclusions. You may simply have fragile capillaries, which would lead your doctor to suggest that you should not try for multi-orgasms—or even indulge in long-term pleasuring. If he gives you that advice, take it.

Don't let this comment turn you off trying to become multi-orgasmic. *This condition is very, very rare.*

Balancing the Fun

If you're going to ask your partner to contribute to your practice, you should recognize her need for pleasure, too. We'll give you some suggestions that will equalize the pleasure for you both. Masters and Johnson have suggested one position; we have discovered another that works well. You can choose whichever one pleases your partner—and you—the most.

1. The male sits with his back against the headboard of a bed or against the wall, his legs widely separated.
2. The woman sits with her back to him, close against his body, with her legs over his, crossing at the ankle.
3. In this position, the man reaches over his partner, caressing her from her breasts to her vagina, giving her body gentle, nondemanding pleasure.
4. As with male nondemand pleasuring, there should be no requirement that intercourse follows the caressing—but it may, occasionally, if you both want it.

We have found that some of our clients can't use this position because the woman is too tall, her buttocks may be too large, or she may be too heavy. (Or both the man and woman may be heavy.) If it works for you, that's fine. Just remember to take it easy and be gentle, slow, and light with your touch.

THE VAGINAL CARESS

The technique we find most successful we developed a number of years ago, when we found that many of our clients had difficulty with the back-to-chest position. Our position seems to work especially well if we're trying to help the woman achieve orgasm during intercourse. It works as follows:

1. The man sits as described in the previous technique, leaning against the wall or the head of a bed.
2. The woman lies on her back with her genitalia close to his and her legs over his legs.

Vaginal Caress

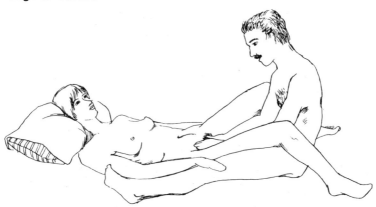

3. The man then caresses the woman's body, paying special attention to the mons (pubic mound) and the clitoris. But he doesn't only touch her there. He strokes her stomach, and down to her knees as well.

4. The man can put a lubricant on his index finger and insert it into the vagina beginning with the fleshy part of his finger up, and his finger straight (unbent), under the clitoris. He should move his finger very slowly but firmly in and out. Then he should gradually and *gently* change the angle of contact, so he touches all walls of the vagina with the fleshy part of the fingertip, paying attention to where his partner most enjoys to be touched. The fingernails should be trimmed closely, and be clean and smooth before this is tried.

5. The woman should tell her partner if she wants a firmer or lighter touch inside her vagina. Many women have to learn to recognize vaginal pleasuring, since they've never had such stroking done before.

6. If you consider that you (the man) are sitting facing a "vaginal clock," you may think of your partner's clitoris as being twelve o'clock. Several inches inside that point is where the Grafenberg spot (G-spot; see page 114) is said to

be located. Some women find this area particularly sensitive to pleasure. Others dislike stimulation in this area.

7. We find that what could be called four and eight o'clock on the lower right and left walls of the vagina are often very sensitive areas in many women. Nerve bundles come together at these two points, and stimulation there results in intense sexual reactions in a large number of women.

Vaginal Clock

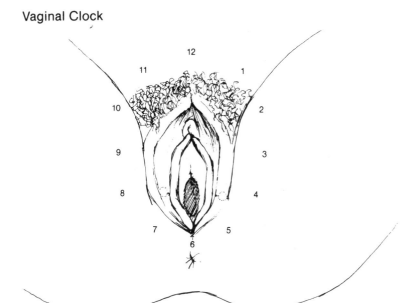

If your partner is not responsive when you first try these caresses, don't despair. Many women consider their vaginas to be sexually "neutral," since they haven't been stimulated enough to develop responses.

We use the exercises, as we have said, to help nonorgasmic women reach orgasm during intercourse. That is the goal of the nondemand touching, too. Even if your partner has orgasms regularly, she can benefit from more caressing.

After all, who can possibly object to being touched in a loving manner?

There is one point to remember, whichever method you choose: You're doing this to balance the pleasure she gives you during your practice periods. Alternate roles. You pleasure her for a while (about fifteen minutes) and then let her pleasure you. Repeat the pleasuring, if you wish. Just remember your reason for doing it. Everything sexual should be enjoyable—never a task you hurry to complete.

When a couple realizes that male multi-orgasm is a possibility, they seem to include it in their thoughts as they exercise. As a result, about a dozen male clients have reported becoming multi-orgasmic during treatment for other sexual problems. In our therapy we don't observe or record clients in nondemand or coitus, and thus we have no observation tapes or charts of their function, but we have had a number of them express their pleasure in their improved sexual response and lovemaking skills.

Tom is one example. He was twenty-six years old when he came to us. His wife was twenty-three. They sought out help because of Sally's frustration.

"Tom never goes more than thirty seconds during intercourse," she explained. "I love him very much, but I know it's beginning to get to me."

Tom agreed. He recognized that if he couldn't change, she would eventually get "fed up," and leave. They both had a certain feeling of desperation regarding the matter, even though she was still quite willing to put up with his quick response.

A second problem had delayed their coming to us. They were newlyweds, and the cost of therapy seemed astronomical. They left after one interview without making a commitment. A few days later, they returned and made a date for a first session.

"We've just decided that this is something that'll affect our whole life together. Nothing's more important, no matter how much it costs." They were even willing to delay buying a new car and a house in order to get their sex life "on target."

Tom was one of our subjects who, in the course of learning the squeeze technique, found himself developing multi-orgasmic abilities. By the end of his treatment, he was going thirty minutes without ejaculating. He would have several "dry" orgasms in that period, and his wife was now having orgasms for the first time during intercourse.

We asked this couple to evaluate their treatment on a scale from 0 to 100. They both agreed that it rated a 150. "We achieved so much more than we expected," they explained, "and we feel so much closer than we did before."

They voiced feelings that some of our other clients have difficulty expressing. Sam, for example, merely mentioned his new competence in a report we requested on the success of the daily assignments we had set for him. After giving the rating for the day and the rest of the report, he added, "Oh, by the way, I had multiple orgasms today." He was a man of few words, and that was probably the longest spontaneous statement he made during his entire treatment program. He and his wife had been married about twenty years (he was forty), and he was obviously pleased, as was she, with his new ability.

11

The Rewards Are Great

Why would a man want to learn to be a better lover? What if his wife seems willing to accept what he does now? Why should he work hard to change? Why is it important to become a more caring person?

There has to be a lot in it for him, that's certain. And, of course, there is.

Caring more means sharing more. Caring means paying attention to your partner's feelings and needs. It means recognizing that your pleasure and arousal can be a source of pleasure for another. Essentially, it is expanding me-centeredness to we-centeredness. It results in great personal enjoyment. If it didn't, if there weren't rewards, few men would take the trouble to change.

So what is the reward?

The reward comes in your own personal enjoyment. Sex never was and never will be entirely physical. There are other feelings that enter into it. Good sex comes when you give up your need for personal control and flow with the sensations you have. You let yourself feel an awareness of your partner's pleasure, and that increases your own. You share a new warmth, a new feeling of value. As you give love, you receive it. You *share* the pleasure of sex, perhaps for the first time.

Does it matter whether your partner is a spouse, a "one-night-stand," heterosexual or homosexual? Not at all. If you learn how to be a good lover (someone who can give love), you may find that your partner will also improve.

Recognize just what your values are. If you do not want to have sex before you marry, yet you want to be capable of showing your great love to your new wife when you do, then you must deal with the need to masturbate. You must master the skills of loving without involving a conflict with your morality. Even a man who prefers to be a virgin when he marries can follow this path.

We have found that men who "hang loose," sexually, are more apt to be willing to exert themselves to become good lovers. Those who hold personal morality as a defense against using masturbation for release or in the process of learning to be multi-orgasmic are often rigid people. They also tend to be self-critical, reproaching themselves for sins they imagine they have committed.

Do you have to be a "swinger" to free yourself from such fears and inhibitions? Not at all. Many swingers are not really comfortable with sex. Sometimes they are trying to prove that they are free of hang-ups that they actually find very confining.

If you are to achieve the most in your sex life, you must aim at becoming comfortable with your own sexuality. And that's why, throughout this book, we have repeatedly returned to the subject of masturbation. A man who is at ease when he masturbates is apt to be comfortable when he has sex with a partner.

Let Your Partner Do Her Thing, Too

This means that when she is pleasuring you, she should be allowed to do it her way.

1. Accept what she does unless it's painful. If it hurts, let her know it.

2. Let her experiment with the use of her hands, her mouth, her breasts—any part of her body. She should have fun, too.

3. Never underestimate the power of your partner—or her skill at making love. Once you make it clear that you're learning, give her a chance to try new things, too. Creativity in sex is great fun.

4. Don't *demand* that your partner think of what to do next, if she finds that difficult. If she hesitates, suggest that she try some of the exercises we've described. You'll both enjoy the nondemand pleasuring exercises, or the body caressing.

5. Take responsibility for your own pleasure. Don't let yourself get tied into one technique. That makes sex monotonous. You want to make it—and keep it—exciting.

6. Let your partner know with sounds—not necessarily with words—how much you like what she's doing.

7. Don't try to pleasure each other at the same time until you've had some good long sessions of nondemand sex enjoyment. Mutual foreplay is not the same as alternate pleasuring.

8. Never put a limit on the joy that is possible when: a) You pleasure yourself; b) Your partner pleasures you; c) You mutually pleasure each other.

9. If you can think of any way to make your partner enjoy pleasuring you, do it. Make her comfortable. Return the pleasuring later—but don't rush to get to the place where both of you are pleasuring each other at the same time.

10. Pay attention to what your partner does when she pleasures you. Often she does to you what she'd like to have you do to her, but she may be too shy to ask you directly.

11. Be a good receiver. Giving sex pleasure loses its fun if the person who receives your gift does not show appreciation.

Let yourself revel in your pleasure. Don't just say "that feels good," and then go on to something else. One of your goals in these exercises should be to learn to appreciate pleasure.

Even in this, there must be mutuality. You must each take responsibility for your own enjoyment. Tell each other what feels good, and then help each other make whatever is going on more pleasurable.

Albert, a recent client, talked about his girl during an early meeting. "She's terrific. But when we have sex, she expects me to do all the work. She wants me to concentrate all of my attention on her. We kiss, and when we have intercourse she moves a little. But she will never touch my genitals, and she won't get on top."

We asked if he had ever talked to her about this, and he said yes. "I've suggested that she should be more active, but she says she doesn't intend to try to be different than she is." He gestured uneasily. "I've been with other women, and they're great. They touch my penis—and even kiss it. And they get on top, and move around. If Karen doesn't change, I guess I'll have to move on. I like being with her, but sex is important, too. If I stay with her and she doesn't change, I know I'll begin looking around for someone else, and that isn't fair, either."

Karen persisted in her stand, and Albert finally left her. We understood. She refused to consider sex as a mutual thing. To her it was what her grandmother had considered it—"something a man *did* and a woman *endured.*"

Multi-Orgasms During Intercourse

We'll go over a few points again. When you begin to try to transfer your multi-orgasmic ability from masturbation to intercourse, we suggest that your partner be on top. That will allow you to relax. It will also let her move more and control the depth of your thrusting. You will not improve your performance by slamming into her. Gentleness is the key to success. Gentle movements, gentle thrusts.

If your partner is on top she can also direct the position of your penis in her vagina. She may want to have it touch her so-called "G-spot" (page 114) on the top wall of her vagina, near her bladder. Some women find this particularly pleasing. This would be at what we mentioned earlier as the "twelve o'clock" position.

Dr. Arnold Kegel reported the especially sensitive sexual spots at what might be called the four and eight o'clock points. He found that if the finger was inserted up to two joints, the fleshy tip would generally touch the most responsive point. You'll find other sensitive places, too, unique to your partner, if you explore her body with the same concern and interest you showed in yourself when you were working on the masturbation exercises.

Remember this: Many women—your partner included —learn to accept themselves as sperm recepticals. That's all many men consider them to be. If you've read this far, you probably aren't that type of man. You want your partner to be far more. You want her to feel loved. So put the emphasis on gentleness, tenderness, and caring. Be aware of the signals she gives you. Accept the fact that she may be too hesitant to actually talk about her sexual desires. There are few situations in life where a women is used as often as in sex. And you want to stop that practice with the woman you love.

If you do that, you'll be rewarded. She will respond by paying equal attention to your responses. We find that if a man is willing to take the time to become aware of his body and its functions, he will develop a greater appreciation of his own pleasure. You can develop this skill together. You can each learn to let your body have its say. And we find that when a man does this, he seems to become multi-orgasmic so naturally that he is surprised at how easy it becomes.

A Few Reviews

Keep yourself in good physical shape. People who are into exercising like jogging, walking, cycling, and tennis tend to do better sexually. Besides, sports are fun, too. You'll find that as you improve the condition of your body your pleasure in living increases. Most multi-orgasmic men are into some form of physical exercise on a regular basis.

Chuck is a good example of this. He is on a regular exercise regimen. He's been jogging for five years. He's twenty-eight, and he's been running five miles a day for the last three years. His body is in good shape, and he dares to ask things of it that would be impossible were he flabby and weak.

He had no difficulty developing the control of the PC muscle that is so important for multi-orgasms. So get yourself back in shape if you've let yourself go a bit. You'll be amazed at how much better you feel, and how much easier it will be for you to achieve your sexual goals.

When you're concentrating on your own responses, masturbate. Don't ask your partner to put up with hours of focusing on your needs and ignoring hers. There'll be time enough to bring someone else into your activities when you've mastered multi-orgasms and can control your erections and ejaculations. Then you can explore the joy of mutual pleasuring on an equal basis.

When you're pleasuring her, focus your thoughts and feelings on her. To help you do this, keep your attention in the here and now. Focus on your reactions and on the reactions of your partner. A good lover takes pleasure in a relationship in which he can give pleasure. If he isn't enjoying what he does, his "giving" will soon dry up.

What's the G-Spot?

There has been a lot said lately about the G-spot, sup-posedly located about a full finger's length into the vagina right on the roof (or top), directly behind the pubic bone. We have not found consistent responses in our female sub-jects to caressing there. Some like it very much. Others find it uncomfortable. Nevertheless, since many women are curi-ous about the spot, we suggest that you try caressing there, just to give your partner a chance to discover how she reacts.

In our studies of subjects, we have found several women who insisted they had G-spots, and who seemed to respond well to caressing there. However, we are not at all sure that they were not simply anxious to get more clinical attention by claiming to have the "latest" trigger to super sex.

We have not been able to locate any specific spot on any of our research subjects. We are continuing our investigation of this subject, and if we do find a definite spot that reacts as the Grafenberg spot is supposed to react, we will publish that information.

In the meantime, you may wish to do a bit of experi-menting yourself. If you want to try to locate the elusive G-spot, this is what you should do:

1. Insert the first two fingers (index and middle) of either hand *gently* into your partner's vagina.

2. Point the fleshy part of the finger upward and to-ward twelve o'clock, as we described on pages 104–05.

3. Explore directly upward with your fingertips along a corrugated ridge that protects her urethra. This will require your pushing in as deep as you can.

4. Pull your hand out slowly, pressing your fingers against the front wall of her vagina until you're touching her pubic bone.

5. Repeat the procedure. This time keep your other hand outside her body, opposite the one inside your partner's vagina. Press downward until you can feel your fingertips "meet."

6. Follow your partner's directions. She may have some idea where you should touch to please her most—and that may be the magic G-spot.

7. Be prepared to accept the fact that your partner may be one of those women who doesn't like having this spot stimulated.

We find that most women prefer what we call the vaginal caress, described on pages 103–05. Whatever you do, don't try to prove theories. You're together for pleasure, not for scientific research. And don't forget that any arousal is most effective after a long period of body and genital caressing and pleasuring.

Some Women Can't Take It

We were surprised when we first encountered a woman who was actually opposed to her partner's multi-orgasmic abilities. She protested when we were interviewing her and her partner before accepting them into therapy.

"Why can't he be like other men?" She seemed very upset. "I talk to the women in my bridge club and they tell me the whole thing's over in five or ten minutes. But I have to get a man who just goes on and on."

Here was the perfect example of the woman who believes that sex is a duty for a woman and a pleasure only for the man. She had never learned to relax and enjoy her body. Nor could we do much to change her. She felt "put upon" when her husband became multi-orgasmic, because he "dragged the thing out so long."

She also seemed to feel that unless he behaved just as her friends' husbands did, he was "strange." Conformity was important to her, even in sex.

Her attitude was common among women only a generation or two ago. We realize that there is always some hangover from past ideology. But such people, in this day when human pleasure is finally being accepted as good, are pathetic throwbacks to a Victorian past. They deserve our pity, not our anger or censure.

What If You Still Aren't Multi-Orgasmic?

Some men may never reach that goal, even though they practice dutifully every day. But that doesn't mean they won't get something out of this book.

Consider this: During your practice, you've probably learned to extend your pleasure and that of your partner by being able to go longer. If you and your partner are enjoying what you're doing, that's all that matters.

Another thing: You may continue with your PC exercises because they give you more control and make you feel good. You may keep them up for months—or maybe even years. And then, one day when you've almost forgotten why you started it all, the "flip over" will occur. You'll be there. Remember, we said at the start that there is no particular time limit to this process. It can happen within a week—or it can take much much longer.

Do you have a different problem? You may have lots of orgasms in quick succession when you masturbate, but you are unable to transfer it to intercourse. Well, don't worry about that, either. Other men have had the same "problem." One, as we mentioned earlier, was certain that he'd be able to when he formed a permanent relationship with a loving partner. Others have made the transfer only after they felt very comfortable with what happened, and when they became convinced that their partners were at ease, too.

One interesting phenomenon occurred more than once during our studies. A woman has a very strong vaginal contraction during orgasm, so strong that it is "picked up" by the recorder in her partner's anus, giving the impression that he has had an orgasm, too. Sometimes he even feels added pleasure because of the tight spasms of his partner's vagina.

In our research, it's important to know exactly what actually happened. But is it just as important to the partners who are experiencing the sex? Certainly not! What matters to them is that they are sharing pleasure.

What must always be most important to you is the pleasure you and your partner are enjoying together.

Our Subjects Give Suggestions

One of our subjects, who had had many conversations with us about multi-orgasms but who for a long time seemed unable to achieve them, told us of his eventual success. "I found that the key to it all was not to withdraw. I had an orgasm, but instead of letting that end things, I just kept on going. I think everyone could do it. It really isn't that hard." His multi-orgasms were as real as any, but he achieved them by having more orgasms after ejaculating—and recognizing that "dry orgasms" were as important to him as his first "wet" one.

Another man sang the praises of the PC muscle. Both he and his partner had strong pelvic muscles, and they tightened them when he felt the need to control ejaculation. It worked for them, and he was convinced that "anyone could do it."

Yet another subject ejaculated, but found that he could continue intercourse (and have more orgasms later) if his partner just squeezed tightly with her PC muscle, holding for fifteen to twenty seconds. Again, he was convinced that "anyone can do that. It's fun—and easy."

Will, another subject who has his orgasms that way, does admit that his first orgasm is his best. This is the usual response we get from men who have this pattern. We have found that a man who can control his ejaculation in his earlier orgasms seems to find increased enjoyment in each subsequent orgasm. They build in intensity, just as women's multi-orgasms do.

This is the program to follow: 1) Exercise as we've described; 2) Accept sex and masturbation as natural pleasures; 3) Be willing to relax and enjoy. If you follow this advice, you'll improve your sexual satisfaction—and that of your partner—very quickly.

From then on, whatever you do will be just that much more icing on the cake.

12

Is All This So Very New?

We're sure you've wondered. We did. If multi-orgasms for men have been possible all along, how come no one talked about them before?

Logically, if all we've said is true, then we can't be the first people to notice such a remarkable phenomenon. In fact, to a certain degree, we ought to be able to prove what we claim by showing that multi-orgasmic men have existed in the past.

To test this, we went back into ancient literature, and we found just what we had expected. As far back as 2968 B.C., in China, there were writings that described male multi-orgasms. The problem, of course, is that when you read the works of some ancient author—written in a language foreign to you—there can be difficulties with translation and interpretation. Maybe we were interpreting what we read so that it reinforced what we believed had been true. After all, we couldn't go back to those long-dead Chinese and test their responses on our machines and charts.

So we continued on with our research, hoping to find something more definite than graceful poetry and flowing lines of ancient calligraphy. When we found our research thinning, we took a different approach.

A hundred years ago it was assumed in Western culture

that only women of questionable morality had orgasms and enjoyed sex. "Good" women accepted sex as an inevitable part of marriage, but they never let on that they enjoyed it (if they did), and like that one client of ours, they endured patiently until it was finished.

In our culture today there have been improvements in that attitude. Far more women today have orgasms and acknowledge them than did even as little as twenty years ago. However, even now, far less than 100 percent of Western women have that open, accepting attitude toward their own sexuality.

Once single orgasms became known and acceptable for women, multiple orgasms occurred occasionally, too, though in very few women. This was true basically because men seldom continued intercourse long enough for a woman to have one orgasm, let alone two or three.

It has really only been within the last forty years that female orgasms have been recognized and accepted as "normal." Since that time, research has shown that women who are capable of having one orgasm, if they continue on with stimulation, will have many, one after the other, until they stop out of sheer exhaustion.

Now it appears that all women are potentially multiorgasmic.

This statement is accepted by most researchers, and by sexually aware laymen. Research that has taken place in the last twenty years seems to prove this.

Yet, during all this research, few questions have been asked regarding male orgasmic capabilities. Why? We suspect that the same inhibitions that confined women for so long to the role of "receptical" for male sexual satisfaction, also put limits on male sexual enjoyment. The accepted concept used to be that humans did not deserve—in fact had no right to have—pleasure in this life. "Eternal joy" was reserved for heaven.

To reconcile the need for sex (people had to continue to

have children, or the world would end) with this concept of the world as a "vale of tears," intercourse had to be limited. Only for procreation, and only one orgasm (with ejaculation) at a time. Sex was a duty for both man and woman.

If we accept modern males as victims of the same attitudes that inhibited women, then we can understand why so many men today still believe that they can have only one orgasm in any one sex encounter—and why research had simply accepted as fact what no one has bothered to disprove.

Once more we returned to old writings, looking for any evidence, no matter how slight, that something other than the presently accepted quick ejaculatory pattern of two minutes (for male orgasm) had been noted, either by poets, by writers, or by whatever "scientists" existed at the time.

We found what we had hoped for. And yet . . .

The problem still existed, as it had when we read the ancient Chinese prose. The method of description was so different from ours that a clear picture of what was happening during sexual activity was not clear.

Take, for example, the Oneida Community, in our own United States. A "simple" description of the phenomena by the granddaughter of the founder of the community is so complex that we, researchers accustomed to technical descriptions of physical acts, were more confused after we read her work than we had been before.

Part of the problem, we decided, lay in the fact that we were reading descriptions of highly personal experiences. If you consider how difficult it would be to describe snow (without the use of pictures) to a person who had never seen it, you will understand how difficult all this can be. An emotion is even more ephemeral than snow.

When a Western doctor first tried to give information on contraception to natives in a primitive society who believed that children were conceived when a woman stood too close to a wooden stick wrapped with string, he was met with derisive laughter. "Everyone" in that community knew that such ridiculous precautions would never have any effect at all.

So we found that the attitude of the reader of ancient works colored the meaning of the words he read because of his own beliefs. A man who is convinced that orgasm and ejaculation are synonymous will view any literature that discusses prolonged intercourse in a different way than will a man who is aware that orgasm can and does occur without ejaculation.

It is from this second framework that we will consider the literature from the past, recognizing that some other reader, coming from the first assumption, would interpret things differently. Our approach is based on what we have observed in our study subjects, and is reinforced by the physiological recordings on our eight-channel Beckman R411 dynograph recorder. We've seen the "pictures" of male multi-orgasms, so we are willing to believe—in fact we know—that they exist.

Starting with this premise, we looked for specific characteristics in the descriptions of sex that exist in old writings.

1. We looked for descriptions of long sessions devoted to sexual pleasure. That, we know from our research, is necessary for multi-orgasm in both men and women.

2. We looked for a society that accepted male sexual pleasure as good. We acknowledge that in most cultures, both ancient and modern, it is male pleasure or satisfaction that is valued.

3. We also looked for cultures where a certain amount of romanticism was evident in the writings of the wealthy upper classes. Those were the societies where sexual enjoyment was most likely to be appreciated for both men and women.

4. We looked for societies where the wealthy classes had a great deal of leisure time.

Why this concentration on the condition of the upper classes? Because throughout most world history the lot of the poor has been hard. They have never had spare time in which to cultivate sensual pleasure.

How Far Back Did We Go?

The earliest information on prolonging sex that we were able to locate came from the Emperor Hiang Ti, in China, in 2968 B.C. We assume that other cultures neighboring China at that time may well have shared in this source of physical enjoyment, for some of the writings suggest this. That would mean that we might find some data in the early Persian writings, and in the traditions and works of ancient India.

If we allow ourselves to follow what was then a natural trade route, assuming that with trade would go cultural knowledge, we might find some concepts of extended sexual pleasure appearing in the works of Middle Eastern cultures and Greece. There is concrete evidence that such trading took place, with China as the motivating force. So we may at least consider the possibility that concepts of extended sexual pleasure that appear in India and Persia and ancient Greece all originated in China. You will find a number of books listed in the Bibliography that will give you more information about these cultural interchanges.

Did these ancient writings use the same terminology we use today? How simple our research would have been if they had. No, they spoke of extended sex in many ways. To clarify what we say later, we'll list the different terms used. We'll also give a description that fits the ancient writings.

1. The Tao of Loving. This, the earliest mention of extended sex, is closely connected to some of the religious practices of that time. The writers of the *Tao of Loving* believed that if ejaculation was controlled, a man enjoyed better health and suffered less debilitating effects when he indulged in intercourse to ejaculation.

In some books, we even found proscriptions for sex that were based on the age and physical health of the subject. All of these writings advised careful control of ejaculation, but put no limit on intercourse or orgasm. It appears that retrograde ejaculation was sometimes mentioned—and considered acceptable.

2. Tantra, the Secret Ritual. In India, this form of religious-sexual practice was considered especially sacred. The steps to be performed are clearly described. Often tantra does not even include penetration, and the accent is on extending the time of "ecstasy." This is a very ritualistic form of sex, deeply tied to religion. It is often equated with the Chinese Tao of Love by various authors, but Jolan Chang, the author of a definitive book on the subject, indicates that tantra is connected to religion in a far more stringent way than is the tao of loving. We feel that there is, certainly, a close connection between the two, not only in the behavior advocated, but in the admonitions given to would-be practitioners. Though the tao of loving does appear to have been less structured, the religious aspects of it appear to us to be as strong as those in tantra.

3. Tantra, the Yoga of Sex. In his book *Tantra, the Yoga of Sex,* Omar Garrison describes the series of steps that, when followed, bring on an extended pleasurable sensation described as "feeling like an energy flow from one body to another."

Recently, when doing research with this ritual, we found that the breathing pattern and the pelvic contractions used were an important part of the ritual. Our subjects were not monitored by a recorder, so all we have is anecdotal information. Our subjects did not report what occurred as an orgasmic experience, but they did report a feeling that energy was flowing between them.

According to the directions in *Tantra, the Yoga of Sex,* no penetration needs to occur, and the ritual must take place five days after the cessation of menstruation. This experience, obviously, was not to be enjoyed any time, but had to be performed at a specific time, and involved specific ritualistic behaviors that culminated in genital apposition without penetration.

4. Vajroli. Vajroli, discussed by Robert de Ropp in his book *Sex Energy,* is a method whereby a man can gain control over the urinary bladder so that he can dilate the sphincter at will. When he can do this, he can consciously direct the ejaculate into the bladder (retrograde ejaculation). This method of avoiding "normal" ejaculation is utilized in Tibet as well as in India.

5. Coitus Prolongatus. This form of extended intercourse is described by Allen Edwards and R. E. L. Masters in their book *The Cradle of Erotica.* It is a very strenuous form of sex, involving extreme willpower and great potency. The movements are continuous, and appear to require great athletic ability on the part of the practitioner.

6. Vishrati. This is the name given to prolonged coitus in classical India. The erotic literature of India as well as that of the Chinese and the Japanese praise the male who can go for long periods of time.

7. Twenty-Times Copulation. This appears to be simply the ability to go for a long time in coitus. It is a term used only in India.

8. Coitus Obstructus. In this technique, described in Reay Tannahill's *Sex in History,* the male presses firmly on a spot between the anus and the scrotum, using the middle finger of his left hand. At the same time, he must gnash his teeth and inhale deeply (but not hold his breath). This technique was believed to force the ejaculate into the brain. What it apparently did was force the semen into the bladder (that old retrograde ejaculation again), to be expelled during urination.

9. Imsak. Little is written or known about imsak. Sir Richard Burton mentioned it in his writings, but no book has ever been published on its methods. Muhammad was said to practice imsak.

Allen Edwards says that imsak is an Arab word meaning "prolongation of pleasure in coition by protracted penetration and withholding of the ejaculation."

The practice of imsak (apparently a form of coitus reservatus) among the Arabs was probably imported from India or China, inspired by the concept that semen is a life force that should not be wasted. For this reason, coitus without ejaculation was frequently practiced. Is was claimed, however, to be highly pleasurable, which suggests to us that orgasm did occur.

The Ali Khan was said to practice imsak. He could go indefinitely, had sex frequently, but was purported to ejaculate only two times a week. Consider the fact that the Ali Khan lived in this century, and was thought a great lover and ladies' man. Other contemporary "cocksmen," who had reputations for "being able to have sex all night," were Errol Flynn, Porfirio Rubirosa, and Gary Cooper.

Incidentally, Allen Edwards notes that men who are unable to practice the retention of seminal fluid are viewed contemptuously by both Muslim and Hindu women.

In *The Cradle of Erotica,* Edwards and Masters note that in the technique, used in both Muslim and Hindu societies, the penis is inserted without movement, but there is stimulation of the clitoris, and the woman contracts against the penis with her pelvic muscles. They note elsewhere that some movement is acceptable.

With such lack of agreement even in one research, we must assume that there are two methods. Maybe the first, where no movement is permitted, is used for learning, as it is today in sex therapy. There is a method called the *quiet vagina,* where the penis is inserted and the couple lies quietly without movement. This is used to help men who ejaculate prematurely, or who wish to learn to go longer during intercourse (for its own sake, or in an attempt to become multi-orgasmic). If this technique parallels the imsak without movement, then possibly our later instructions to use movement as soon as control is reached is like the second kind of imsak found by Edwards and Masters.

10. Coitus Reservatus. This is probably the most common name used for the phenomenon of prolonged intercourse, although the name is of recent origin. Apparently, orgasm takes place, in the form of retrograde ejaculation, since this type of sexual behavior is usually described along with a discussion of how to retain the semen in the body. One author, Paul Gillette, in *The Complete Sex Dictionary,* claims that there was no movement during the sex approved by the Oneida Community, so male orgasm was prevented. The Oneida group seems to have used this method, with or without movement, and it not only appears to have had no bad effects, it seems from reports by members of the society that men who were skilled in it had better health than that of the general population.

Better overall health care, however, may be a more realistic explanation for the longevity of the men in the Oneida Community. In her book, *Oneida Community: An Autobiography, 1851–1876,* Constance Noyes Robertson notes that good health is an important aspect of communal living. She does not state definitely that retrograde ejaculation was used by this community, since the information available is not adequate to make any definitive judgment. Inge and Sten Hegeler, in *An ABZ of Love* (Medical Press, New York), when mentioning the Oneida Community, imply that no sexual gratification of any kind occurred.

Coitus reservatus was said to be a way of making love to a partner that produced intense pleasure for both. It allowed the male to function with a number of partners, one after the other, which was important especially in the Middle East and the Far East, where men had harems or concubines. Among the Oneida Community members were encouraged to have many partners, so the same need for extending the lasting powers of the male might have existed.

In a way, the structure of the Oneida Community resembled that of a swinging group today. A man capable of being multi-orgasmic, in a swinging group, can enjoy many partners during an evening, and ejaculate only with the last. A few such men have reported to us that they sometimes have more than one orgasm with one partner during the evening, as well as having orgasms with several other women within about a four-hour period.

11. Chira. Chira is mentioned in Vatsyayanas' *Kama Sutra, the Hindu Art of Love.* However, no description is given. It is simply described as coitus that goes for an extended period of time prior to ejaculation.

12. Maithuna. This is another name used to describe coitus reservatus. The origin and culture are unknown, but the name does appear in literature, often interchangeably with other terms used to identify the prolongation of intercourse. Often the terms aren't really identical in meaning, though they are used in the same way as coitus reservatus.

13. Kebbauzehs. This is defined in Scott-Morley's *Encyclopedia of Sex Worship* as a method a woman used to contract her vaginal muscles so that copulatory movements were not necessary for orgasm or ejaculation. Such a technique would appear to be not only possible, but quite effective. We know that a man can go longer during intercourse if he takes a more passive role. In our therapy, we often suggest that the woman take the superior position and also the initiative in pelvic movements as part of the practice used to help her companion last longer. We've also found that a number of female subjects have used their pelvic muscles during intercourse, and in so doing have helped their partners become multi-orgasmic. This, however, was done on their own, not at our suggestion.

14. Male Continence. This is another term that was used in the Oneida Community. It appears to have originated during the middle of the nineteenth century, and a book was written on the subject by Noyes. This is a term that was actually used by members of the community. What precisely is meant by it, however, we do not know.

15. *Dynamic Coitus Prolongatus.* Edwards and Masters describe this as meaning repeated and energetic acts of sexual intercourse. It's performance depends entirely upon masculine potency, sensitivity, and willpower. Movements are strenuous and continuous, and suspension of thrusting lasts only a few seconds during the act itself.

16. *Dharanaratt.* This is described by Edwards and Masters as copulation prolonged with erotic tension maintained for a long period of time. Neither orgasm nor ejaculation are said to occur. (The fact that these two are mentioned separately seems to indicate to us that they were viewed as separate phenomena.) A man was said to be able to have pleasurable intercourse with as many as twenty women without loss of arousal. This practice seems to produce an altered state of consciousness in a male, giving him a "high" that lasts for an extended period of time.

17. *Karezza (or Carezza).* Alice Stocham, an early feminist and an advocate of birth control at the end of the nineteenth century, apparently coined the term karezza. She wrote a book called *Karezza: Ethics of Marriage,* which was a modern adaptation of the early taoist and tantric love techniques. Tannahill, in *Sex in History,* likens karezza to the Chinese and Indian technique of having orgasm without ejaculation. She also suggests that karezza was practiced in the Oneida Community. If so, it was probably used mainly as a birth control technique, since ejaculation was not involved.

All of these methods, similar as they may be, have small differences that make each one unique. Yet our information regarding them is sparse. Even the most recent practices are shrouded in a haze that makes it difficult to understand. We do know that the Oneida Community permitted its members to choose partners from the group, and was opposed to any bonding that excluded the group. But it is difficult for us to learn much about the frequency of sexual contact in the community; some literature describes sexual license with varied partners as occurring frequently, while others emphasize abstinence as a more common practice. In any event, we do know that the Oneida Community produced few children in the twenty-five years it existed.

We have one description of karezza, from Scott-Morley's *Encyclopedia of Sex Worship,* in which it is stated that there is no movement. This indicates that it is more like tantric yoga than tao. Morley-Scott provides this explanation of the act:

> Karezza (also Carezza) intercourse between a male and female in which no coital movements are used, taking an hour or more to perform, is an act of will on the parts of both the male and female. It sometimes ends with spontaneous and unified orgasm between the both of them, in which the male lets loose a vast quantity of stored up and held-in-check sperm and the female's vagina contracts violently while her clitoris becomes vibrant and agitated.

18. The Mystic Way. A Dutch writer, R. L. Van Gulic, in his book *Sexual Life of Ancient China,* spoke of the "mysticism of coitus reservatus." He was at least honest in his presentation. He admits that he does not understand the concept, even as he attempts to explain it.

19. The Alchemy of Ecstasy. There are, obviously, marked differences between various methods of prolonging intercourse, even though some writers have lumped them all together. The alchemy of ecstasy utilized the retention of semen, that we know. But by that is it meant that retrograde ejaculation was practiced? We cannot say. As with other concepts originating in the East, this involved control of breathing. What part did it play in the technique? Again, we cannot say. All we know is that the retention of semen and the conscious control of ejaculation were part of this sexual "exercise."

Nowhere in all the literature we studied were men referred to as multi-orgasmic. Yet in our studies, we have found that when a man extends intercourse for more than fifteen minutes, usually there occurred at least one orgasm, and often more. Were such orgasms part and parcel of all these various techniques? We can only guess at the answer.

Orgasm Versus Ejaculation

We do know from our experiments that orgasm and ejaculation are not inextricably tied together, and so we have not been surprised to find that some literature supports our findings. Kinsey reported that male children up to puberty have orgasms but don't ejaculate. He also found that older males, either because of age or a slowing down of the sexual processes, sometimes do not ejaculate. Mellaril, a medication taken by many men these days for hypertension, is well known for its ability to inhibit ejaculation. But it does not usually hinder orgasm. In literature, the laboratory, and medicine, there are clear indications that the two, orgasm and ejaculation, need not be considered inseparable.

Why the Big Secret?

Over past centuries, the population of the world has been segregated into the very wealthy ruling class and the very poor lower class. Many of the pleasures enjoyed by the upper classes were not available to those in lesser positions. Often religion forbade things to the poor that the rich took for granted.

To some degree this was a result of the unequal distribution of leisure time. The underprivileged poor had no time for extended pleasure. Their time was taken up with the task of finding food and paying for shelter.

Reading, too, was taught only to the wealthy, who could then discover these sexual pleasures by studying the ancient writings. Again, the poor were denied that opportunity. All the literature we found spoke of kings and rulers, of emirs and shahs. Obviously, in the past, this form of sexual indulgence was not for the common man.

The poor man had only one use for sex—procreation. In most cultures, even today, prejudice against liberal sexuality often restricts people with less money and/or education in their attempts to improve their sex lives. The roots of inhibitions and prejudice lie deep.

What Prejudice?

Whenever procreation is important, as it was as long as mortality was high and most infants died at birth, semen has great value. This reverence for the "life fluid" reaches far back into history. There was a time when a farmer would spill some semen on the ground to make his land fertile. And rain was called "God's semen" by many primitive peoples.

In areas where, even now, the belief in the sacredness of semen continues, the practice of coitus reservatus is very acceptable. In the past, procreation was the most important reason for coitus. Pleasure came in a poor second, especially for women. Therefore, we find far less information than we would like in most ancient writings. Often it is restricted to prohibitions against homosexuality, prostitution, getting an unmarried woman pregnant, and other such rules that control procreation. There can also be found some admonitions to women as to how they should behave with their husbands, the number of wives a man was allowed, and, occasionally, instructions as to how long intercourse should go on.

The Bible

The Bible does make reference to length of intercourse, and the ability of a man to satisfy many partners. Both King David and King Solomon were evidently very potent, virile men. David was said to have had intercourse thirteen times in succession in one evening. The inference is that each was a separate occurrence (not multi-orgasmic in nature), since his wife washed herself after each ejaculation. Samson was said never to stop ejaculating during his sexual activities. This resembles one multi-orgasmic man we have observed in the laboratory, who ejaculates a small amount of semen almost every time he has an orgasm.

Early Iran, India, and Greece

Some literature from early Iran includes tales of men enjoying prolonged pleasure. The stories of Vis and Ramin and that of Khusrau include such events. For the most, however, they describe the trials and tribulations of two lovers, and only touch lightly on the sexual activities in which the pair indulge. In those tales, much is made of platonic love.

In India, according to the literature, Brahmin erotologists, like those in ancient Greece, made a science of prolonged tumescence and delayed orgasm. There are specific instructions that will teach a man to prolong his pleasure artfully for a half-hour or more, "avoiding all haste and thereby conditioning himself for harmonious wedlock." This seems to imply that pleasure was shared, and was considered important for the woman as well as the man. Yet the main emphasis placed on coitus reservatus was directed toward the man's health and well-being, not on his ability to please and satisfy his wives.

We can conclude from this survey that the idea of extended sexual pleasure is far from new. It was, in the past, garbed with much religious ritual and was often restricted to special groups, such as royalty or at least the wealthy. But restricted though it was, it certainly was known—and practiced.

Christian Influence

Most modern Americans are reasonably well acquainted with the biblical admonitions for man to "be fruitful" and to "multiply." We have also learned, for whatever reason, that sexual pleasure is basically sinful. We've already mentioned how the issue of procreation was treated by the early Christian Church. Sex was a duty—but it should not be enjoyed. By enforcing that concept, and by teaching its followers that "things of the body" were "of the devil," the Church managed to keep sexuality under control. Certainly, in most Christian societies, until quite recently, the idea that sex was a natural pleasure that should be enjoyed was rarely found.

However, other things besides religion influence thought—especially today. As a society becomes affluent, pleasure is accepted as a right.

Our society is, basically, a society of plenty. Even our poor have more than was available to poor in past generations. And so, in a very natural way, attitudes have altered. Today we consider pleasure a positive thing, and feel a man or woman is justified in seeking it, as long as it is not at someone else's expense.

We still have other attitudes that hamper us, however, in this new appreciation of pleasure. Some of the concepts we often encounter among our clients are listed below. If you have been inhibited by any one of them, you will find your striving for multiple orgasms easier when you have at last put that unfounded belief to rest.

1) You must not waste time.
2) Time is money.
3) Work is the only truly satisfying activity.

Get over feeling guilty if you spend an hour having pleasure. If you can overcome that traditional, common emotion, you will find your path to all pleasure grows easy. And your chances of becoming multi-orgasmic will be at least doubled. Think of it this way. For generations, sexual pleasure was "hogged" by the rich and the influential. But this is the day of the common man. You have as much right to enjoy your body as King David did.

So do it! Relax. Put guilt feelings aside. And give yourself over to pleasure!

13

Has It Happened Recently?

The answer is yes. We have named a few men, well known to most Americans, who had reputations for being "cocksmen." Ali Khan is, of course, the most notable, but some movie stars of the past were also notorious for their sexual capacities. Yet as a group, Western men seem to have a reputation for ejaculating rapidly after insertion, and the complaint of American women is that this leaves them unsatisfied and frustrated.

Is it, then, a cultural characteristic? Has the "Puritan ethic" so denegrated pleasure that we, their descendents, are incapable of experiencing it without guilt? Is the more relaxed attitude toward sex that is found in Europe and Asia more conducive to the development of multi-orgasmic men?

It would appear so. We have already seen that a great amount of leisure time is needed before the attention of a culture is directed toward physical pleasures. In the past, this leisure was only available to the wealthy, and sexual pleasure was considered sinful by the poor and essential by the rich.

When conception was the main goal of intercourse, the wealthy had to establish some acceptable reason for encouraging extended sexual pleasure, to justify it to their own cultural conditioning. It appears that the theory was developed that the extension of sexual pleasure (including the delaying of ejaculation and sometimes even the avoidance of it) would improve the health of the practitioner. The goal was still ejaculation, but it was controlled, used at the right time. And this rationalization made everything acceptable.

But in our country, as we have said, this concept never developed. We regularly have clients who feel it is essential that they ejaculate, even though they have no desire for children or their partners are past childbearing age. In some of those cases, the man seems to feel that there is a need to ejaculate quickly, as if that somehow proves his superiority as a male. There is a strong bias against pleasure for itself, and a man can accept pleasure when it comes only if it is severely limited.

In a personal conversation with Dr. William Masters, several years ago, we discussed a wealthy American man who had brought his sexually unsatisfied, nonorgasmic partner in for treatment. When he was informed that the solution to her problem was for him to learn to go longer in lovemaking before he had an orgasm, he lost interest. He believed that the quicker a man ejaculated, the more of a man he was. He refused to jeopardize his manhood.

Other beliefs that interfere with Americans becoming multi-orgasmic—or even enjoying sex for long periods—is the idea that ejaculations are debilitating (the old "vital fluid" concept) and should be experienced only rarely. There was a time when boys were warned against masturbation because "every man is given only a limited number of ejaculations. If you waste them, you may lose the ability when you are still young, and never have an orgasm again."

A man who believes this obviously would not dare to risk exhausting his "supply" of orgasms by masturbating to gain orgasmic control. If the fear of "using up" a limited supply of orgasms is coupled with the idea that a man proves his manliness by being quick, a man is thoroughly blocked from ever learning to be multi-orgasmic. However, such men seldom have such a goal.

If, however, a man only wishes to learn to control his ejaculations, it is easy to teach him, at the same time, to become multi-orgasmic. Often such subjects experience retrograde ejaculations, which they find acceptable.

We realize that if we had more data from the past, we might be able to help such men control their ejaculations as it seems the ancients did. Earlier cultures apparently had better methods than we do to control ejaculation and to guarantee retrograde ejaculations. This technique was actually used by some, it appears, as a method of birth control that worked very effectively.

In our experience, however, retrograde ejaculations occur more by chance than choice with the multi-orgasmic men we have monitored. Transurethral prostate surgery produces retrograde ejaculations. Men in our society, however, seem troubled by this, since they feel that ejaculation is necessary for orgasm, and they consider themselves "inadequate" because they can't ejaculate in a "normal" way. Often they complain that ejaculation isn't as enjoyable "that way."

We recently spoke to a research subject, a medical doctor who has worked extensively in the field of human sexuality, who had transurethral surgery. He informed us that his sexual pleasure had increased, and that he had become multi-orgasmic. His wife confirmed what he said. She told us that they now had sex more than they had before his operation, and that sessions lasted longer than they had in the past.

This leads us to believe that were it possible for modern men to learn to control their ejaculations and/or have retrograde ejaculations at will, they would soon be able to vie with the ancients for sexual kudos.

Sex and Religion

We've already seen that in ancient times extended sex seemed to be directly connected to religion. Our puritanical background leads us to assume that all advocacy of extended sex in more recent times is anti-religious. This, however, is not true.

John Humphrey Noyes, the head of the Oneida Community, was an ordained minister. His advocacy of extended sex was based on his religious beliefs, and the entire community had a strong religious "flavor."

How did this tie between religion, which we consider a "spiritual" emotion, and sex, which we consider "physical," develop, especially during periods in history when procreation was important and necessary? We can only guess at the answers.

Our assumption is that since sex was necessary to procreate, and most cultures had god-inspired orders to "multiply," the germ of connection already existed. Then, when people did extend sex—and found that it created a unique feeling of "oneness," they considered that emotion a spiritual feeling. Also, men who have multi-orgasmic abilities often report feeling "high" when they go for extended periods, and such "highs" were considered in the past to be "gifts of the gods."

There is one other consideration: Religious leaders in the past often had more free time to experiment than did their laymen followers. This time, like the time with which the rulers and wealthy men of the past were blessed, allowed them to "discover" the techniques that lead to extended sexual pleasure.

The Oneida Community

Constance Noyes Robertson, granddaughter of John Humphrey Noyes, the leader of the Oneida Community, wrote the most extensive description of the Oneida Community in her book *Oneida Community: An Autobiography, 1851–1876.* Her parents lived in the community, and she grew up there and knew many of the original members.

She stated that male continence was essential to a new group that could not afford children. It was a central theme of the movement, and all men were required to practice it. Learning was not left to chance. Open discussions by the members, where both men and women were free to speak, resulted in the decision that the older persons in the community would initiate the younger ones.

Mrs. Robertson did not specify in her book just how that was to happen. However, it was successful. Two hundred fifty people lived together for twenty-five years, practicing male continence, and they found it an effective method of controlling population. Sexual closeness was part of a general love relationship in the community. Conception was to take place only when the community approved—and then through the mating of genetically chosen partners.

Reverend Noyes is said by his granddaughter to have based his idea for this form of living on the verse in Genesis 2:1. "God made woman because he saw it was not good for man to be alone." However, we have been told of research that indicates he investigated until he devised a method of having sex without conception after his wife, whom he loved dearly, died in childbirth. Conception, he argued, was not necessary in the relationship God set up between man and woman. And in his community, conception did not occur by accident. Only one child was born in the community during the first four years of its existence, so the method they used was obviously effective.

Noyes recognized two kinds of sexual intercourse, "one

simply social and the other propagative," and decided that the propagative kind should be exercised only when impregnation was *intended* and "mutually agreed upon."

Evidently all the men were eager to learn the technique. The community practiced sexual freedom between and among partners, so any man who didn't learn the control had difficulty finding a partner who would have him. This certainly provided the motivation for quick learning.

According to Tannahill, Noyes presented his technique, which he called karezza, claiming ". . . it satisfied men's and women's sexual needs, avoided the excessive and 'oppressive' procreation that was almost universal at the time, and yet did not require the use of 'unnatural, unhealthy, and indecent' condoms, sponges, and lotions which were, of course, destructive to love."

Members of the community considered continence to be a positive factor in their good health and longevity. However, there could be several other explanations that have equal—if not greater—validity. The community provided productive work for all of its members, and productive work seems to have a beneficial effect on people. During World War II, when large numbers of older people became involved in war jobs, the death rate among them went down.

Another factor could be the existence of better medical care in the community than in the society in general at that time. Also, everyone in the community felt strong emotional support, and a feeling of belonging that could increase life expectancy.

In spite of these other possible explanations for the better health of the men in the Oneida Community, we cannot discount the fact that, throughout history, there has always been the suggestion made that the retention of ejaculate contributed to good health. Until that aspect has been thoroughly studied, we can do no more than to recognize its possibility. Also, since no definitive description of the method used in the Oneida Community exists, we are justified in considering the possibility that at least some—if not all—of the men in that group had orgasms without any ejaculation, rather than retrograde ejaculations.

What Makes a Man a "Cocksman?"

In Eastern cultures, where wealthy men had many wives and/or concubines, a man's social standing was enhanced if he was able to keep all his women sexually satisfied. With such motivation, men in those societies had reason to develop multi-orgasmic abilities, or at least to master methods of delaying orgasm for a long time.

In our culture, the motivation is different, but the men who achieve sexual "prowess" all seem to have that same capacity for extending their ability to perform coitus.

We've all read of specific famous legendary lovers who seemed to be able to charm every woman they met. Don Juan, for example, was a man who was able to seduce many women, and was recognized as being able to last for long periods of time during intercourse.

The Life and Loves of Frank Harris is a book about another famous lover, whose only claim to fame was his "way" with women and his involvement in frequent and prolonged intercourse.

We've already mentioned Ali Khan, who had a similar reputation with women, due to his practice of imsak.

Certainly, this ability seems super-normal, yet many men today wish they could possess it. Often, in expressing a desire for greater sexual competence, men seem unable to differentiate between being able to "go longer" and being so attractive to women that they would have their pick of the most beautiful women in the world.

As for the women who enjoyed Don Juan's attention, or the Ali Khan's, or Frank Harris's, they seemed to enjoy themselves thoroughly, so we can assume that when a man can go for a long time, both partners benefit.

You've Got to Breathe Right

You'll recall from the ancient Chinese writings we quoted that breathing affected the stamina of the man. We, too, have found that certain styles of breathing are more effective than others when a man is working to become multiorgasmic. Incidentally, proper breathing also affects a women's ability to orgasm, so this is not something important only for a man.

We've concluded, after studying a number of subjects, that orgasms can be controlled more easily if a man breathes rapidly, or holds his breath as he feels himself approaching ejaculatory inevitability.

Other Factors Affect It, Too

From the readings we have done, we can conclude that in the past if a man only wished to prevent expulsion of his semen, he learned to control the valve that, in normal sexual activity, prevents the ejaculate from going into the bladder. However, we have been unable to find any specific directions for those exercises that would result in such control.

Tannahill suggests that "What this method achieved, in fact as distinct from theory, was diversion of the seminal fluid from the penis into the bladder, from which it would later be flushed away with the urine."

Perhaps that conclusion is correct. However, we feel that in all the literature from the Eastern cultures we read there was no mention of such a practice, nor were directions given for learning the skill. The fact that they believed a man could divert the semen to the brain seems to indicate that they were unaware that it might have gone into the bladder.

We've already mentioned "dry" orgasms, noting that when they occur after a man has ejaculated, they seem less strong than those reported by our multi-orgasmic men who experience them before they ejaculate.

Yet, generally, researchers continue the fallacy that orgasm and ejaculation are synonymous, and to refer to the ancient practices as actually involving delaying orgasm. Alex Cross, in a *SIECUS Report,* volume 10, number 2, of November, 1981, remarks that: "Throughout history, from the proponents of Indian Tantra, Troubadour love practices, at least from different nineteenth-century American variants, and from some prestigious French physicians in modern times, that the practice of extensive pleasurable love acts occur to select people or groups."

He goes on to say that this practice includes the withholding of orgasm, since orgasm ends the sex act. He claims that these practices of withholding orgasm are still used in China.

We had the opportunity to test a Chinese subject who did have multiple orgasms. As with our other multi-orgasmic subjects, he had orgasms without ejaculation that were most satisfying to him. He could have stopped at any time after the first couple of orgasms without ejaculating and been satisfied, even though he had not expelled any semen.

Not All Women Appreciate "Dry" Orgasms

In our culture, as in some others, there are women who feel that a man has rejected them if he fails to ejaculate during orgasm. They cannot believe that a man is properly aroused if he does not expel semen. We have encountered this during therapy, especially with older couples. The wife feels rejected, and tells us that "he must have a girlfriend." One even remarked that her husband didn't love her any more. "If he did, he'd ejaculate." So here again is another possible impediment to a man becoming multi-orgasmic. If either he or his partner feels that ejaculate is essential for a complete act of love, he will have more difficulty learning to have an orgasm without ejaculating.

The Penis Is a Magic Wand

Early man revered and actually worshiped the penis. Its ability to become erect was considered magical. We carry over some of those beliefs in the names men give their penises. A penis is called a *rod,* a *shaft,* a *pole,* a *staff,* a *stick,* and a *wand.* Some of these are the same names that we give to a magician's baton. In biblical references, when a man swore an oath to another man, he placed his hand on his genitalia, to signify the solemnity of his vow. Even though most modern men would not admit to thinking of the penis as sacred, it has become obvious to us in taking sexual histories since 1968 that at least some men do view their genitalia in this light.

Emily, who came to us with her husband for therapy, told us that "It was weird. The sicker I was, the more he wanted sex. I like sex, don't get me wrong, but sometimes I was so sick I didn't really enjoy it. Once when I came home from the hospital and was still really ill, he insisted that we have sex every night. I figured it was important to him; maybe he'd missed me more than I thought. So I went along with it. I did generally feel better afterward, and I managed to orgasm."

She continued. "Then, one night, it all fell together. When we were through he said, 'There, that should make you feel better.' I realized then that he believed he was helping me get well. He really thought intercourse could affect a magical cure, that his ejaculate had magical power."

This attitude on the part of the man has surfaced during other therapy sessions with other couples, so it is not an isolated phenomenon. One young client, Tony, expressed his feelings when he said, "I'll lose my strength if I ejaculate. It will emasculate me."

He was quite involved in Eastern (Indian) philosophy, and had very negative feelings about masturbation. This is not surprising, when you consider that early Indian literature speaks of the importance of preserving the ejaculate.

India is not the only country where ejaculate is valued, however, or where the genitalia are revered. Among the Maori, when a spell was repeated, the person invoking the spell would put his hand on his genitalia to give the spell supernatural powers. This practice occurred in other South Pacific cultures as well. And in Italy, the power of the penis has been transferred to gestures that represent it. The fica, or infamous finger, is an example of this transference of magical qualities. In this gesture, the finger represents the penis and the closed fist the testicles. The same gesture appears in ancient Roman culture, and among the early Greeks.

We've already mentioned the Biblical oath-taking that involved resting the hand on the "thigh," which was St. James' euphemism for the penis. This practice is still practiced in some sections of Morocco.

A book discussing the "Right of First Night," or *Jus Primae Noctis,* noted that the lord of the manor had first sexual contact with a bride, whatever her station. It appeared that there was more to the procedure than simply the dominance of the "lord" over the "minion" and his wish to satisfy his interest in "new conquests." The implication was that this act had magical overtones. This is reinforced by the antiquity of the practice, and by the fact that it is part of many cultures. We have found evidence of it in early Icelandic and ancient Roman literature, as well as in the Talmud. Arab writers, and writers in Scotland, France, Germany, Russia, and many others speak of this ritual.

There are many possible explanations for it. Maybe the older king was considered to have more powerful magic than the young bridegroom, and thus was able to prepare the way through the hazards of "breaking in" a virgin. In any event, this is only one of many references to the potency and importance of the male genitalia. We should not be surprised at their existence. History has been dominated by males since its beginnings.

Today, we have reminders of the transference of the penile powers to the hand in such things as a boy scratching the palm of a girl's hand when shaking it, to signify that he wishes to have intercourse with her.

Therefore, when we discuss with a man the possibility that he change his sexual behavior, as he must to become multi-orgasmic, we often run into irrational objections that are based not on any scientific knowledge but on beliefs from the past that, in spite of his modern education, still affect his behavior. All or some of these attitudes may affect you in your attempt to follow our directions and develop your multi-orgasmic powers. If they do, you will have to face and overcome them before you will achieve success.

14

What Do Other Researchers Say?

We aren't the only researchers who have considered that orgasm and ejaculation might not be one and the same. As early as 1959, contemporary American literature contained information about their separation. H. W. Secor, in an article on "The Facts about Ejaculation" in *Sexology* magazine, published in May of that year, wrote: ". . . although many people use the two terms interchangeably, actually the climax and ejaculation are two different processes, although they almost always accompany each other in the male."

Much of the information we have on multi-orgasmic males was gained during a series of seminars we presented throughout the United States in the mid-1970s. During that time, we came in contact with some ten thousand professionals throughout the country. Whenever we spoke, at least two or three men claimed to be multi-orgasmic—and those whom we were able to test proved they were right. A number of women also claimed to have experienced such partners.

Recently a knowledgeable gynecologist came to us after hearing us speak and congratulated us on our documentation. He explained that he had been teaching men to be multi-orgasmic in order to improve the sex lives of the women who came to him for treatment. He felt that his work had improved the sex lives of the women he treated. His attitude was understandable. After all, his clients were women. However, we feel that women aren't the only ones who gain when a man learns to be multi-orgasmic. The man, too, discovers new depths of pleasure in an act that before occupied only a brief moment. He also has orgasms that are more intense. Surely he gains as much as the women with whom he enjoys his new power.

There was another reference, indirect, it is true, to multiple orgasms in the April 1962 issue of *Sexology*, in the question-and-answer section. A newlywed asked Le Mon Clark, the staff member who wrote the column, about the fact that she had several orgasms during intercourse. He replied that ". . . multiple orgasm is more common in a woman than it is in a man." He said no more, yet he did imply that men could have multiple orgasms. However, nothing more was said on the subject for some years, and no researcher took up the question and examined it more closely.

Kinsey

In fact, Kinsey, Pomeroy, and Martin, in their now-famous study on male sexuality, found that the average response pattern of three-quarters of American males was to ejaculate after less than two minutes of stimulation.

Kinsey and his associates also noted in their study of male sexuality that of the men studied, ". . . 380 have had a history of regular multiple ejaculation at some point in adolescence or in adult years." Note the use of ejaculation, rather than orgasm. Evidently, Kinsey considered the two to have the same meaning. Interestingly enough, though Kinsey referred to "multiple ejaculation" in his reference to repeated orgasms in adolescents and some adults, he still did differentiate between orgasm and ejaculation in his research.

This is because he found preadolescent males, and some adult males who have had certain types of surgery, to have orgasms without ejaculation. He also discovered some males who had several orgasmic reactions before ejaculation took place. We've noted this same phenomenon in our research, as well as occasions when orgasm occurred after ejaculation.

In spite of this research, the recognition of multiple orgasms in males is relatively new among researchers. For that matter, even the ability of women to have multiple orgasms was not considered common by Kinsey, since he noted that 14 percent of the sample he used in preparing his book *Sexual Behavior in the Human Female* did speak of having two or more orgasms at a time. He concluded that though some women appeared to have multiple orgasms, there was much evidence that few could do so.

If a man can have an orgasm without ejaculating, can he ejaculate without having an orgasm? Kinsey did not think so. However, we have encountered a dozen cases or so in therapy where the man complained that he ejaculated without having an orgasm, thus ending his sex session early and with no satisfaction for himself or his partner. However, we suspect that at least some of these men just did not perceive their orgasm when it occurred. In all of the cases, we were able to help the men so they did have orgasms— or learn to recognize them—when they ejaculated.

Kinsey had five cases in his research on males who practiced coitus reservatus. His summation was that: "These males experienced real orgasm, which they had no difficulty recognizing, even if it is without ejaculation." We can't be certain from his report whether these men had only one or many orgasms, nor can we be sure that he studied these men directly. It is possible that he received a report from them during an interview. Doctor Pomeroy informs us that Kinsey did do some observations, and we suspect that these cases may have been among those he actually studied.

Masters and Johnson

Masters and Johnson, in 1966, noted that a few males under thirty years of age ". . . repeated orgasm and ejaculation within minutes, without a long refractory period," and that this phenomenon did not occur with older males. Twelve years later, in personal correspondence, Masters stated that ". . . literally, we have no significant data on truly multi-orgasmic males, if one is visualizing the experience in terms of the female's multi-orgasmic capacity. . . ." It is again important to note that Masters speaks of ejaculation as an intrinsic part of orgasm.

Masters and Johnson did not encounter multiple orgasmic males in their research, but that does not surprise us. They were not specifically looking for this phenomenon, as we have looked for it in our later studies. There is also the fact that recording instruments today are far more sensitive than they were in the fifties and sixties, when Masters and Johnson were doing their research.

We did discover one interesting quotation in Tannahill's *Sex in History:*

> In 1976, the West caught up with the master Tung-hsüan. Ten years earlier the researchers Masters and Johnson had discovered, that, in man, orgasm and ejaculation are two separate physiological processes and that it is possible to experience the pleasure of the first several times, before it need be terminated by the second.

Through personal correspondence with Masters and Johnson we learned that they knew nothing of this phenomenon because they had never researched it. We have to assume that the information came from a lecture, or that it might have come from us or some other research team, and been misinterpreted as coming from Masters and Johnson. Since we know of no other research being done on male multiple orgasm, we suspect that this quote refers to our work, not to Masters and Johnsons, but since we are not certain, we include it here.

Masters and Johnson do refer to one subject who ejaculated three times in ten minutes. They did not report that he had any orgasms, however, though that doesn't mean one didn't occur. It is possible that this subject was multi-ejaculatory but not multi-orgasmic, or it might have occurred when he was not being monitored, and so there was no clear way to determine whether he had an orgasm.

Robbins-Jensen Study

In 1978, Mina B. Robbins and Gordon D. Jensen, in the article "Multiple Orgasm in Males" in *The Journal of Sex Research*, volume 14, number 1, remarked that they had noted a current phenomenon as multiple orgasms in males. Like us, these two researchers recognized that the phenomenon is multi-orgasmic, since orgasm occurs with each ejaculation and also typically without ejaculation.

Certainly we make no claim to having discovered multi-orgasms in men. All we have done is record them and identify them physiologically. The behavior itself appears to be at least four thousand years old.

In mid-1974, after we had studied a number of multi-orgasmic men, Mina Robbins and Gordon Jensen took advantage of our laboratory to study a male subject who was multi-orgasmic. This gave us one more subject to add to our research. In the paper they produced on their research, they claimed that ". . . some men with spinal cord injury or other nerve lesions report a sensation of orgasm without ejaculation . . ."

We agree with their findings. We have records to support orgasmic response in such cases. A paraplegic we studied at first had difficulty having orgasms, and the multi-orgasms he had while on our machines were a new experience for him. However, several months later he reported that, since his experience in our laboratory, multiple orgasms were now a regular part of his sexual function. He has been able to utilize his own experience in his professional work with other handicapped men.

Robbins and Jensen questioned men between the ages of twenty-two and fifty-six, with the majority between thirty-three and thirty-six. The male they studied on our machines was in the upper age grouping. They found that thirteen of the men they interviewed reported orgasms without ejaculation, except for the final orgasm during a given session. This is the pattern we found among our subjects, as well.

Robbins and Jensen ". . . hypothesized that the orgasmic response and the ejaculatory response can be separate physiological reactions in a normal state . . ." This we also found to be true, even in research where our subject did not fall in a "normal" category, for example, a subject with certain physical handicaps or of an age where ejaculations might not occur with each orgasm. The majority of our subjects were in good health, and some were joggers or regular exercisers.

The year that the Robbins-Jensen paper was published, Dr. Hartman presented a paper on multi-orgasmic men at the Western Psychological Association meeting in San Francisco. At the same time, a San Francisco editorial writer made caustic comments about Robbins's and Jensen's research, and considerable negative space was given to the idea of multiple orgasms in men. The editorial suggested that it was a shame that professional people wasted their time on such a crazy idea.

Brecher—the Sex Researchers

Following the Robbins-Jensen study, Edward M. Brecher included information on multi-orgasmic males in an expanded edition of his book *The Sex Researchers.* Brecher had talked to us about the phenomenon, as well as to Robbins and Jensen. He stated:

> Multi-orgasmic males reported that they had consciously learned how to curb ejaculation at orgasm. . . . During the learning process, the men had had to stop thrusting at crucial moments, or to breathe more deeply than usual, in order to control ejaculation while continuing to experience orgasm. As the learning process progressed, however, and as they experience multiple orgasms reliably over a period of months, these men reported that "they generally needed less or no conscious effort to control ejaculation compared with their earlier experiences."

Konnoff Studies

Nick Konnoff, a student at California State University Long Beach, computerized data from our research records in 1978 on the psychosexual characteristics of three groups of men: multiple orgasm, single orgasm, and sexually dysfunctioning. The data came from male sexological forms on the subjects. Each group contained twelve men, for a total of thirty-six.

Konnoff identified the three groups as multi-orgasmic males (MOM), non–multiply orgasmic males (NMOM), and sexually dysfunctioning males (SDM). For more details of these classifications, see the Appendix.

He found that multiple-orgasmic men were "more functional overall sexually than are non–multiple orgasmic men." They had less difficulty with premature ejaculation, had better self-concept if their partner did not orgasm, were able to maintain an erection for longer periods of time after penetration, and were less repulsed by all areas of their partners' bodies (which might indicate that they were less inhibited).

Drawing on his own experience in our laboratory, Konnoff wrote a second paper, as yet unpublished, on "How to Become Multi-Orgasmic." In it he suggests masturbation in the morning before rising and again in the evening. "Have coitus with a partner if that option is available to you. In all situations where there is penile stimulation, it is important that an attempt be made to go as long as possible. Lots of foreplay and nondemand pleasuring of the male will help to increase the sexual arousal and response."

Other suggestions he made are these:

1. Stand with legs eighteen inches apart and raise and lower the testicles with your pelvic muscles. Do this seventy to one hundred times a day. As with the exercises we suggest, he recommended that you begin with a lesser number and gradually increase it.

2. You can recognize the pelvic muscles by stopping the flow of urine. Do this by sitting on the toilet, not while standing. This way, he says, a man can learn to do the same exercise when sitting anywhere.

3. Masturbation should be done while lying down.

4. The erection should be maintained as long as possible.

5. Tensing the legs and lower abdomen, as well as the pelvic muscles, can extend the period of erection.

6. Use a vibrator during masturbation. (We also find a vibrator helpful. A man and woman can have fun with a vibrator, as well as its being valuable to a man when he is alone.)

7. Continue intercourse after ejaculation. It will work as a learning experience in becoming multi-orgasmic.

8. Learning to maintain a hard, fully erect penis for an hour or more and to bring the PC muscles under voluntary control helps in stopping or avoiding ejaculation.

9. The amount of foreplay is directly proportional to the number of orgasms a male can achieve. (This may be true for Konnoff, but we have not found any such relationship.)

10. Quantity of ejaculate in no way reflects the intensity of orgasm. (We tend to agree with this, though we feel that much depends on personal interpretation of the rating scale.)

11. Konnoff refers to a study by D. O. Cauldwell, who wrote a pamphlet entitled "Sexual Athletes": ". . . multiple orgasms, in the strictest sense of the word, means more than one orgasm with the same erection. In a small number of cases there are males who are capable of having more than one orgasm and consequently more than one ejaculation before losing an erection." Cauldwell observed thirty males who had from six to ten orgasms. They were all preadolescent males, and there was no ejaculation in any case. In all, he examined 182 preadolescent males.

J. Jones Stewart, a gynecologist and obstetrician concerned with anorgasmia in his female patients, began working with their spouses on helping the men last longer in coitus. In the process he began to find that some of the men began reporting multiple orgasms. One of his experiments with these men involved the use of condoms to catch any ejaculate with orgasm prior to a final ejaculation. What he found was that early orgasms contained no semen, although all other visible signs of orgasm occurred and were reported by the subject. He therefore concluded, as we have, that orgasm and ejaculation were separate entities.

Unfortunately, no studies have been conducted yet on the neurochemical muscular transfer of orgasm and ejaculation. Lennart Nilsson did some remarkable studies of this kind ten years ago, but the orgasm-ejaculation phenomenon was not part of the study. When these studies are done they are expected to show that orgasm and ejaculation are two separate entities masked by their simultaneous occurrence in most men.

Hartman and Fithian Research

We cannot end this chapter without citing our own research on the subject of multi-orgasmic males. We have observed 740 volunteer research subjects, 282 of them males. Of that number, 33 were multi-orgasmic.

This brings up an interesting point. In our report on Kinsey, we mentioned that in his 1948 studies he found that 14 percent of his female subjects were multi-orgasmic. Current studies today indicate that over 50 percent of the women studied are multi-orgasmic. As for men, Kinsey noted only that he had encountered multi-orgasms in prepubescent boys and in "a few older men." In this light, our research findings that 12 percent of the men we studied in the research laboratory are multi-orgasmic. This seems to indicate that, as sexual attitudes become more permissive, both men and women increase their ability to be multi-orgasmic, with men following behind the women, since they started up "the ladder" of greater sexual expression later than did the women.

Our first multi-orgasmic subject was monitored in 1974. He had heard us lecture and he talked to us about his multi-orgasmic ability. At that time, we merely speculated that men should be able to be multi-orgasmic. Since then, we have found that 12 percent of our male subjects are multi-orgasmic, as we mentioned in the previous paragraph. This high percentage may be due to our known interest in the matter, since men who believe they are multi-orgasmic come to us seeking corroboration. We have no way of knowing whether it might not be, in fact, indicative of the number that exist in our culture.

We have monitored all of our multi-orgasmic subjects on a nine-channel recorder. By early 1982, we had monitored the thirty-three subjects we have mentioned previously. One was studied and recorded on eighteen different occasions, and most of the others have been studied at least several times, both during masturbation and coitus.

Our most frequently monitored subject had twelve orgasms in close succession, then, after stopping, he decided to try again and had four more. These were actually two separate "events," with a loss of erection between them, and was not typical of his response or of the other men we studied. Nevertheless, like any exception to a pattern, it pleases us to have a record of it. The average number of orgasms a man had during our research is four. Some men had as few as two, and one had sixteen.

The multi-orgasmic males we have studied come from various cultures. We have recorded a multi-orgasmic Palestinian from Israel, an Englishman, a Chinese, a Spaniard, and an American black. We have also monitored a multi-orgasmic American who was born and raised in China, and two severely physically handicapped men. We feel that our sampling is reasonably representative of our larger group of research subjects, which also includes blacks, men from other countries, and some handicapped. A complete report on this research, with full scientific data, will be published later, in a more scientific manner than would be of interest to the general reader.

What you can see from this report is that we may have the largest sampling of multi-orgasmic men on record, but we are certainly not the only researchers interested in the subject. The entire matter seems to us to be a concept whose time has once more arrived. After all, in a culture in which even the poorest man has time to experiment with sex, we should soon reach a new golden age in America, where extensive sexual pleasure is available to all.

APPENDIX

Laboratory Evidence

In researching response patterns in the laboratory on a Beckman R411 dynograph, with both males and females, we found that males and females both responded in the same way. All parameters changed and physiograph records had to be identified not only by name, but also by sex, to differentiate male from female records.

The early records made of females showed them to be singly and multi-orgasmic with variations of this pattern. If we looked at the heart rate, which is the clearest and easiest parameter studied, the single orgasm appeared to be similar to a bell-shaped curve. Normally the heart rate at base, or at rest, will be about 70 beats per minute, going up to 120 or thereabouts at orgasm and then returning to 70. Orgasm was usually reported and noted at the peak; there were variations on the theme, depending upon the anxiety and physical condition of the person. Pelvic contractions coincided with the elevation of heart rate at orgasm.

Some women had several of these peaks and valleys, which we call *discrete multiple orgasms.* That is, they started at a baseline, reached a peak, and returned to baseline before they returned to a peak again.

Female Single Orgasm

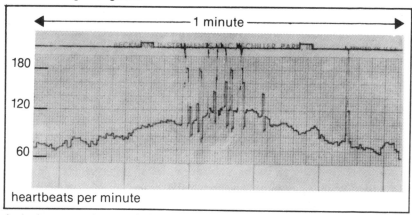

A single orgasm is recorded at the cardiac peak of 120 heartbeats per minute.

Female Multi-Orgasm—Discrete

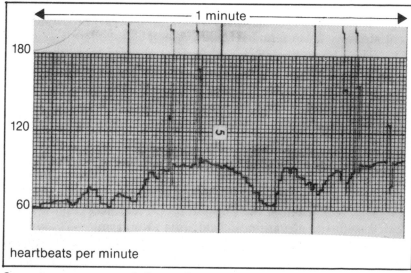

Separate orgasms recorded one minute apart during continuous masturbation.

We encountered other women whose patterns differed: Their heart rate didn't return to baseline, but stayed high and reached a number of rapid peaks, which we and the women identified as orgasms. This we called a multiple orgasm, continuous.

Still other records combined a number of discrete orgasms and a multi-orgasm continuous combination phase.

We have studied thousands of female orgasmic responses, but the number is much smaller for men. The record for a single orgasm in a male looks very much like a single orgasm in a female. Although there is considerable consistency in the records of an individual, no two records will look exactly alike. We call that phenomenon *fingerprinting effect*.

Female Multi-Orgasm—Continuous

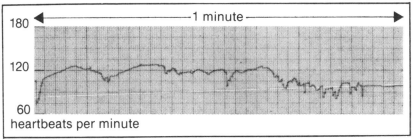

Three repeated orgasms recorded in less than two minutes with continual high heart rates of approximately 130 beats per minute.

Female Multi-Orgasm—Combination

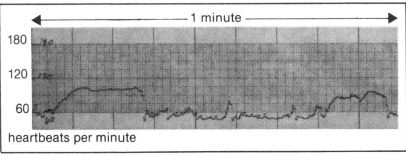

Two continuous orgasms followed by a return to baseline for several minutes and then a discrete orgasm.

Similarity of Male and Female Orgasms

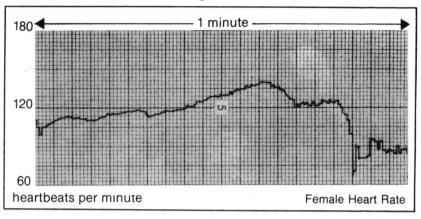

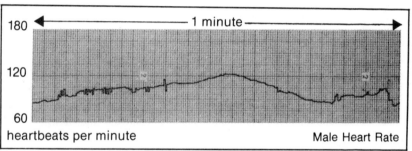

Single cardiac peak orgasms showing similarity of pattern.

In the sample of 455 females run in the Center laboratory, some were able to have orgasm fairly rapidly, the shortest being three minutes. The average time tended to be close to twenty minutes, and some took almost an hour before their first orgasm was achieved. Sex is a physical activity. It takes a great deal of energy, effort, and stamina to achieve orgasm. Those who don't achieve orgasm often give up. Achievement of orgasm is a learned behavior, and people who have difficulty doing so often have not learned the various road marks that get them there easily. Those that reach orgasm rapidly know what to do, and do it, so orgasms are easy for them.

While researching, our next thought was this: Since women are singularly and continuously multi-orgasmic and male and female genitalia develop from the same embryonic tissue, was it not possible that men could also be multi-orgasmic? Physiologists and other experts we consulted with said no because a man ejaculates when he has orgasm —a finite amount of ejaculate puts a limit on number of orgasms. Mrs. Fithian felt that did not settle the matter since male and female function were so much alike and came from the same embryonic tissue; it seemed unlikely they would be so different in regard to multiple orgasms.

Several things then happened at approximately the same time. About 1970 a newspaper article said that males taking the drug Mellaril had retarded ejaculation. We encountered two atypical clients in therapy; one had ejaculation without having orgasm, and the other had the sensation of orgasm but didn't ejaculate. It became obvious that ejaculation and orgasm were not the same thing, and that you could then have one without the other. It stood to reason that males could be multi-orgasmic just as females were.

The subsequent ten years of research and working with more clients with these problems have shown this to be true. We have also found, in reviewing early literature, various references to Kinsey's work and his findings on the separation of orgasm from ejaculation.

In comparing male function to that of the female the following records can be compared with the previous female patterns. The more typical male pattern of orgasm is the single orgasm, just as it is in females.

In those males who are multi-orgasmic, various patterns emerge just as they did in the female. The following male record shows a series of discrete male orgasms. With this particular subject, ejaculation did not occur at each orgasm, although ejaculation may occur with each orgasm or some orgasms and not others, depending upon the research subject.

As you can see, the multi-orgasmic male patterns are

Male Single Orgasm

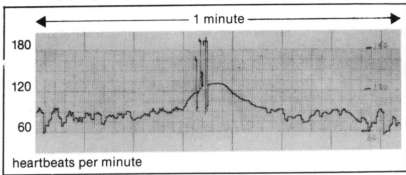

Recording of single orgasm at cardiac peak of approximately 120 heartbeats per minute.

Male Multi-Orgasm—Discrete

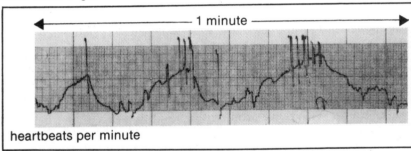

Three successive orgasms recorded in close proximity but with return to cardiac baseline between each orgasm.

Male Multi-Orgasm—Continuous

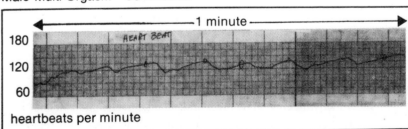

Three orgasms recorded with no return to cardiac baseline between orgasms.

similar to that of the female. We know much more about female responses since we have so many more records of female orgasms to study, and multi-orgasmic male responses are fewer in number. We do have a sufficient quantity of records to realize that multi-orgasms are more common than has generally been considered. The fact that multiple orgasms are learned also makes them teachable.

Male Multi-Orgasm—Combination

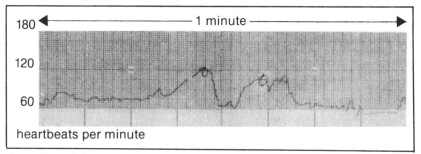

Recording of single orgasm at cardiac peak with a return to baseline followed by two continuous orgasms with no return to baseline between them.

Pelvic Muscles

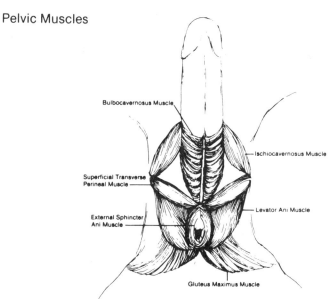

Retrograde Ejaculation

Retrograde ejaculation occurs when the ejaculate goes back into the posterior urethra and on into the bladder, rather than into the anterior urethra and out through the meatus of the penis in the usual way.

Surrogate Partner

A surrogate is a professionally trained male or female provided by the therapist for an unmarried person who has no partner during the intensive phase of sex therapy.

Important Muscles

The bulbocavernosus helps to control urination and assists during erections. This muscle encases the penile base. A second muscle also helpful in producing an erection is known as the ischiocavernosus. Also important are the transverse perineal muscles. Maintaining good pelvic health through exercise of these muscles aids greatly in obtaining and maintaining erections and assisting in multi-orgasmic function.

Precoital Fluid

The Cowper's glands secrete an alkaline fluid that produces lubrication of the urethra so that sperm can easily move down and out.

During arousal in the male there may be an oozing of this fluid. Some women find this objectionable. Ejaculation and precoital fluid are part of normal arousal-response patterns, however.

Erections

An erection is the stiffening or hardening of the penis caused by the flow of blood into empty chambers or cylinders in the penis called corpora cavernosa.

When sexual arousal occurs the penis elongates and thickens. A small penis when flaccid usually increases in size more than a large flaccid penis, so that penile size tends to even out at erection.

During the early phases of the sexual arousal process the testicles will elevate toward the body.

As a man ages the penis may not make as extensive a swing from a flaccid to erect state.

Konnoff Studies

He identified the three groups as: the multi-orgasmic male (MOM), nonmultiply orgasmic male (NMOM), and the sexually dysfunctional male (SDM).

He defined the multi-orgasmic male (MOM) as "the male with the ability to have more than one orgasm and/or ejaculation during coitus or masturbation without detumescence of the erect penis with a brief or no refractory period at all between succeeding orgasms." The term *multiple orgasmic* implies that there may or may not be an ejaculation with each succeeding orgasm.

The data indicated that "in general, multiply orgasmic men are more functional overall sexually than are nonmultiple orgasmic men." Among the differences were less difficulty with premature ejaculation, better self-concept if the partner did not orgasm, the ability to maintain an erection for longer periods of time after penetration and less repulsion by all areas of the partner's body, which might indicate less inhibition.

Penis Flaccid and Erect

 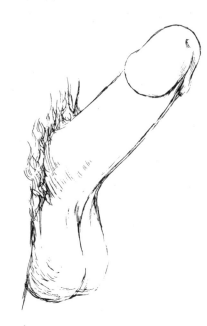

Masturbation Machines

Reference in the text to either portable or console-type masturbation machines refer to those manufactured by;

FUNWAYS INC.   FUNWAYS INC.
P.O.Box 9691   *or* 15424 Cabrito Road
North Hollywood,   Van Nuys,
California 91609   California 91406

Film or Book

The Center for Marital and Sexual Studies has produced a
film entitled *Multi-Orgasmic Male.* It is available for sale or
rent for professional use only. The book *Treatment of Sexual
Dysfunction* by William E. Hartman and Marilyn A. Fithian is
also available.

Inquiries for film or book should be addressed to:

Center for Marital and Sexual Studies
5199 East Pacific Coast Highway, Suite 503
Long Beach, California 90804

DAILY RECORD CHART

NAME: _____

WEEK BEGINS _____

Please record the number of times each of the following behavior occurs daily. In order to be precise, it is important that each event be recorded on a daily basis. At the end of each week the data from this time period should be mailed to us, and a new checklist started. Any instance of sexual behavior MAY comprise several of the rows. Select the ONE row that best describes the behavior and check only this row unless other rows are directly related, i.e. 10 and 11. More rows may be checked if they occur during the same day. If erection only occurs when lying on back or is lost when moving from back, please state. If any medication was taken within any twenty-four-hour period, please state kind.

	MON	TUE	WED	THUR	FRI	SAT	SUN
1. Sexual dream (write dream on back)							
2. Sexual fantasy (write fantasy on back)							
3. Nocturnal emission							
4. Morning or other erection, no masturbation, no sex play*							
5. Erection with masturbation,* no sex play							
6. Masturbation with ejaculation,* no sex play							
7. Erection with partner,* sex play							
8. Ejaculation with partner, sex play							
9. Intercourse							
10. If intercourse occurred, degree of erection on a scale of 0 to 10							
11. If intercourse occurred, estimate length of time							
12. Pelvic exercises, flicking							
13. Tightening and holding							

COMMENTS: We would like to know: 1. Any difference or change you may perceive in a physical, emotional, psychological, or perceptional way, or anything else you feel may be important. If you have a partner, what differences have you noticed in her? Use the other side of this sheet to answer, if necessary.

*List degree of erection on a scale of 0 to 10, with 10 being a full erection. Length of time an activity went.

BIBLIOGRAPHY

Allgeier, Elizabeth Rice, and A. R. Allgeier. *Sexual Interactions.* Lexington, Massachusetts: D. C. Heath & Co., 1984.

American Medical Association. *Human Sexuality.* 1972.

Annon, J. *The Behavioral Treatment of Sexual Problems.* Honolulu, Hawaii: Enabling Systems, 1974.

Beigel, Hugo G. *Sex from A to Z.* New York: Stephen Daye Press, 1961.

Block, Iwan. *Strange Sexual Practices in All Races of the World.* Trans. by Keene Wallis. New York: Falstaff Press, Inc., 1933.

Brecher, Edward M. *The Sex Researchers,* Expanded Edition. San Francisco: Specific Press, 1979.

Chang, Jolan. *The Tao of Love and Sex, The Ancient Chinese Way to Ecstacy.* New York: E. P. Dutton, 1977.

Chow, Eric. *The Dragon and the Phoenix, Love Sex and the Chinese.* London: Michael Joseph, 1971.

De Ropp, Robert S. *Sex Energy.* New York: Delacorte Press, 1969.

Douglas, Nick, and Penny Shigis. *Sexual Secrets; The Alchemy of Ecstacy.* New York: Destiny Books, 1979.

Edwards, Allen, and R. E. L. Masters. *The Cradle of Erotica.* New York: Julian Press, Inc., 1963.

Edwards, Allen. *The Jewel in the Lotus.* New York: Julian Press, Inc., 1964.

Garrison, Omar. *Tantra: The Yoga of Sex.* New York: Julian Press, Inc., 1964.

Gernsback, Hugo. "Question and Answer Section." *Sexology* magazine. March 1959, April 1962.

Gillette, Paul. *The Complete Sex Dictionary.* New York: Award Books, 1969.

Goldberg, B. Z. *The Sacred Fire.* New York: University Books, 1958.

Hartman, William E., and Marilyn A. Fithian. *Treatment of Sexual Dysfunction.* Long Beach, California: Center for Marital and Sexual Studies, 1972; New York: Jason Aronson, 1974.

Hegeler, Inge and Sten. *An ABZ of Love.* New York: Medical Press of New York, 1963.

Hite, Shere. *The Hite Report.* New York: Macmillan, 1976.

Marcus, Irwin M. "Masturbation." In *On Sexuality,* Toksoz B. Karasu and Charles W. Socarides, eds. New York: International University Press, 1979.

Kinsey, Alfred C., Wardell B. Pomeroy, Clyde E. Martin. *Sexual Behavior in the Human Male.* Philadelphia: W. B. Saunders Co., 1948.

Kinsey, Alfred C., Wardell B. Pomeroy, Clyde E. Martin, Paul H. Gebhard, et al. *Sexual Behavior in the Human Female.* Philadelphia: W. B. Saunders Co., 1953.

Konnoff, Nick S. "Ways of How to Become a Multiple Orgasmic Male." Unpublished paper, 1980.

Konnoff, Nick S. "Psychosexual Characteristics of Multiply Orgasmic Males Versus Non-Multiply Orgasmic and Sexually Dysfunctional Males." Unpublished paper, 1979.

Ladas, Alice, Beverly Whipple, John Perry. *The G-Spot.* New York: Holt, Rinehart, and Winston, 1982.

Masters, William H., and Virginia E. Johnson. *Human Sexual Inadequacy.* Boston: Little, Brown, 1970.

McCary, James L. *Human Sexuality,* Third Edition. New York: Van Nostrand, 1978.

Moses, Eugene B. "Questions and Answers on Premature Ejaculation." *Sexology* magazine, November 1958.

Netter, Frank H. *The CIBA, Collection of Medical Illustrations: Volume 2, Reproductive System.* CIBA Pharmaceutical Co., 1954.

Nilsson, Lennart. *Behold Man.* Boston: Little, Brown & Co., 1974.

Pomeroy, W. B. *Boys and Sex.* New York: Delacorte Press, 1968.

Physicians Desk Reference 1974. Oradell, New Jersey: Medical Economics Co.

Physicians Desk Reference 1984. Oradell, New Jersey: Medical Economics Co.

Robbins, Mina B., and Gordon Jensen. "Multiple Orgasm in Males." *The Journal of Sex Research,* vol. 14, no. 1, pp. 21–26. February 1978.

Robinson, Victor, ed. *Encyclopedia Sexualis.* New York: Dingwall Rock Ltd., 1936.

Robertson, Constance Noyes. *Oneida Community; An Autobiography 1851–1876.* New York: Syracuse University Press, 1970.

Robertson, Constance Noyes. *Oneida Community; The Breakup 1876–1881.* New York: Syracuse University Press, 1972.

Scott-Morley, A. *Encyclopedia of Sex Worship,* volumes 1, 2, and 4. London: Walton Press, 1967.

Secor, H. W. "The Facts about Ejaculation." *Sexology* magazine. May 1959.

Sealy, Shirley. *The Celebrity Sex Register.* New York: Simon and Schuster, 1982.

Shahin, Bishara. Unpublished paper. United States International University, 1983.

Stone, Hannah and Abraham. *Marriage Manual.* New York: Simon and Schuster, 1937.

Suriew, Robert. *Sarve' Naz.* Geneva: Nagel Publishers, 1967.

Tannahill, Reay. *Sex in History.* New York: Stein & Day, 1980.

Tripp, Dr. C. A. "Good Questions." *Forum* magazine, p. 12. October 1982.

Vatsyayanas. *Kama Sutra, the Hindu Art of Love.* Trans. by S. C. Upadhyaya. Bombay: D. B. Tarapvevala Sons & Co., 1961.

Wallace, Irving, Amy Wallace, David Wallechinsky, Sylvia Wallace. *The Intimate Sex Lives of Famous People.* New York: Delacorte Press, 1981.

Westermark, Edward. *The History of Human Marriage,* volume 1. London: Macmillan & Co., 1921.

Wolfe, Linda. *The Cosmo Report.* New York: Arbor House, 1981.

Zilbergeld, Bernie. *Male Sexuality.* Boston: Little Brown & Co., 1978.

INDEX